PREFACE

The purpose of this book is to give the reader an appreciation of the type of weather which may be experienced under certain conditions and in this respect a number of weather maps have been drawn and described. It is impossible to cover every type and frequently the prevailing pressure pattern will be seen to be a combination of a number of separate pressure systems.

The weather indirectly controls one's way of life and is something from which it is difficult to escape. It has no boundaries, either geographical or international, although the near presence of land or open water may bring about changes in the weather that is being, or is likely to be experienced.

It is hoped that the layout will appeal, since it deals initially with the different types of weather maps and their associated weather; a more detailed explanation of the formation and causes of wind, cloud, rain, fog and other phenomena follow towards the end.

The contents will be of particular value to the yachtsman, whether studying for a B.O.T. Yachtmaster's Coastal Certificate or just enjoying the pleasures of coastwise sailing. Although having a slight nautical bias, weather forecasts and maps printed in newspapers or broadcast through the media of radio and television are available to everyone, and, it is hoped that this book will appeal to all who have an interest in the subject of meteorology.

HOOK END, Essex   G. W. White

October, 1967

CONTENTS

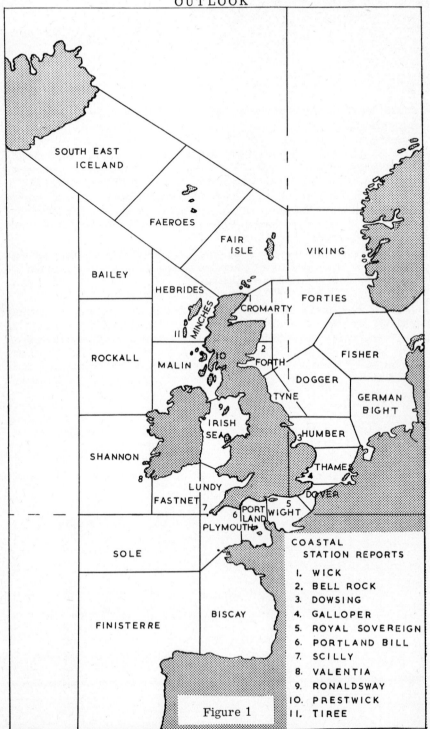

Figure 1

OUTLOOK

WEATHER MAPS
and
ELEMENTARY FORECASTING

by

G. W. WHITE

KANDY PUBLICATIONS LIMITED

by the same author

EXERCISES IN COASTAL NAVIGATION

Set and designed by the publishers and litho printed for them
by the Westwood Trading Co. Ltd., South Croydon, Surrey

U.K. Standard Book Number
85309 020 3

First published 1967 by

KANDY PUBLICATIONS LIMITED

Kenley, Surrey, England

1

SHIPPING FORECASTS

Weather forecasts are issued in a variety of ways to suit the requirements of the general public. They are printed in the majority of the daily newspapers and are also broadcast on both the radio and television.

Those of direct concern to the seafarer are the weather forecasts issued by the Meteorological Office for the use of seamen. These forecasts cover the North Sea, the English Channel, the Irish Sea and the North Atlantic seaboard and are broadcast by the B.B.C. and certain G.P.O. Coastal Radio Stations. Figure 1 shows the sea areas covered by these Shipping Forecasts.

The following notes give a brief outline of these services but the reader is advised to consult the latest edition of Reed's Nautical Almanac, or similar publication, for precise details relating to the working frequency, the times of transmission and the areas covered by the forecast from the various transmitting stations.

B.B.C. BROADCASTS
The weather forecast for shipping is broadcast by B.B.C. Radio 2 (Light Programme) on 1500 metres (200 Kc/s) and V.H.F.

The broadcast, in general, contains the following information:-
- (a) Warning of Gales.
- (b) A General Synopsis.
- (c) A Forecast for the next 24 hours for Coastal Areas.
- (d) The latest reports from certain coastal stations and light-vessels.

The B.B.C. Television Service transmits a forecast chart of the prevailing winds and visibility for coastal areas of the British Isles at the end of the evening programme.

G.P.O. COASTAL RADIO STATIONS
Plain language area forecasts covering the next 24 hours after the time of issue are broadcast from British Coastal Radio Stations on R/T. The R/T transmission is first broadcast at conversation speed and then repeated at dictation speed. These broadcasts cover the coastal areas adjacent to the transmitting station.

GALE WARNINGS
These are only issued when winds of force 8 or gusts of force 9 and above are expected. The wind strengths refer to the Beaufort notation, see page 94. The term "severe gale" implies a wind of force 9 or above. The terms "imminent", "soon" and "later" indicate gales within 6 hours, between 6 and 12 hours and more than 12 hours from the time of issue. The date and time of origin are given in each gale warning broadcast.

Gale warnings are promulgated as follows:-

(a) Visual Warnings

Visual signals, cones by day and lights at night, are exhibited at certain coastal stations. See page 126 for a description of the various signals in use.

(b) B.B.C. Broadcasts

Gale warnings are broadcast in the Shipping Forecast as mentioned previously and also on Radio 2 (Light) on longwave, medium wave and V.H.F. at the first programme juncture after the receipt of the gale warning. The announcement is preceded by the words 'Attention all Shipping'.

If the B.B.C. Radio 2 programme is being broadcast on more than one service, gale warnings will also be heard on that service. These warnings will also be heard on V.H.F.

(c) G.P.O. and Irish Coastal Radio Stations

Gale warnings are broadcast by the station appropriate to the area within which the gale is expected. The broadcast is initially at conversation speed and is then repeated at dictation speed.

ADDITIONAL B.B.C. BROADCASTS

During the herring fishing season (October and November), for the benefit of the East Anglian Herring Fishing Fleet, special forecasts are added to the shipping forecast for an area of about 30 miles radius around the 'Smiths Knoll' lightvessel. This area follows that of the 'Thames' coastal area in the shipping forecast. For the benefit of the Scottish Fisheries in the Minch Area a special forecast is included in some of the broadcasts on weekdays.

The precise times at which the above B.B.C. broadcasts are made are published in the Radio Times.

SPECIAL SHIPPING FORECASTS

Special weather forecasts for a period up to 24 hours from the time of issue may be obtained from the Meteorological Office on request and local weather forecasts within the vicinity of a port may be obtained from the forecast centre nearest to the port.

Reports of the present weather prevailing at specified places may also be obtained by telephone from a number of Coastal Stations.

Information relating to the above forecasts is given in the Admiralty List of Radio Signals, Volume 3, and also in Reed's Nautical Almanac.

WEATHER FORECASTS FROM CONTINENTAL STATIONS

Certain continental stations broadcast storm warnings and weather forecasts for shipping in the English language. For instance, Ostend (Belgium) gives details of storm warnings and weather forecasts in the English language for the sea areas Belgian Coast, Dover and Thames.

Full details relating to the Radio Weather Services broadcast by foreign stations can be obtained from the appropriate volume of the Admiralty Radio Signals and to a certain extent Reed's Nautical Almanac.

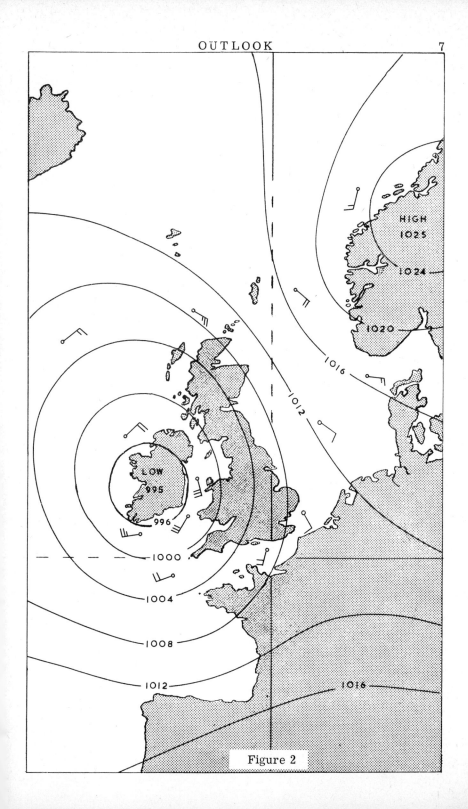

Figure 2

2

PRESSURE AND TEMPERATURE

It is necessary, in order to obtain the maximum benefit from a weather forecast, to draw a weather map depicting the general distribution of pressure, winds and associated weather. Certain terms used in meteorology must therefore be understood before such a map can be drawn.

The following general synopsis is an example of the type heard in the shipping forecast and figure 2 shows the associated weather map depicting the general distribution of pressure and winds.

A general synopsis:-

"A depression situated over southwest Ireland is expected to drift slowly northeast whilst an anticyclone persists over Scandinavia."

A "depression" is an area of low barometric pressure and an "anticyclone is an area of high barometric pressure. The terms "low" and "high" are relative values used when drawing a comparison between the pressure in one area and that in another area. In this particular case the pressure is high over Scandinavia and low over southwest Ireland.

ATMOSPHERIC PRESSURE

This is the force exerted by the atmosphere at any point on the earth's surface and is measured by means of a barometer. Accurate readings are obtained with a mercurial barometer but for compactness, as is necessary in small craft, an aneroid barometer will give a degree of accuracy sufficient for the needs of yachtsmen. The pressure is usually measured in millibars but occasionally the readings are given in inches.

Weather maps show the horizontal distribution of pressure over the surface, all readings being given for a common datum which is that of the mean sea level. Barometer readings taken at heights other than this level must therefore have a height correction applied to them. Serious differences may arise if this correction is not applied, especially when making a comparison between barometer readings.

This effect is shown in Figure 3 where two observers are near to each other regarding their horizontal distance apart but are at different heights. The observer at 'A' is at sea level whereas the observer at 'B' is at a height of 120 feet above sea level.

The pressure at B (P') differs from that at A (P) by the weight of the column of air between them, namely the area shown shaded (P - P'). The atmospheric pressure near the surface decreases approximately one millibar for every 28 feet ascent. Since the vertical separation between A and B is 120 feet, the reduction in pressure (P - P') is almost 4·3 millibars. If the pressure at A is 1004 mbs. then the pressure at B would be 999·7 mbs. and it is necessary to correct the pressure at B by this difference to obtain the correct mean sea level pressure.

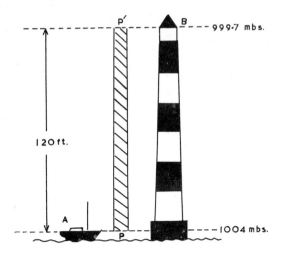

Figure 3

The lines drawn on the weather map through places having the same mean sea level pressure are called 'isobars'. In Figure 2 it will be seen that the isobars are drawn at intervals of 4 mbs. i.e. for 1004 mbs., 1008 mbs., etc. Isobars never cross each other and are frequently found to form closed curves around an area of high or low pressure. Notice how the isobars enclose the area of low pressure over southwest Ireland. Isobars on a weather map are similar to the contour lines on an Ordnance Survey Map.

THE STRENGTH AND DIRECTION OF THE WIND

Wind is the horizontal movement of the air over the earth's surface when there is a difference in atmospheric pressure between two localities.

The wind strength depends on the pressure gradient which is related to the perpendicular distance between the isobars. An analogy may be drawn between the pressure gradient on a weather map and the steepness of the ground on an Ordnance Survey Map. Closely spaced contour lines indicate a steep incline whereas widely spaced contour lines a gradual incline. Isobars spaced closely together give rise to a strong or steep gradient and strong winds. Widely spaced isobars indicate a slack or weak pressure gradient and relatively light winds.

The spacing of the isobars on a weather map therefore gives an indication of the wind strength that may be expected in any locality. When drawing a weather map the strength of the wind as given in the forecast will assist in the spacing of the isobars.

The direction of the wind is ascertained from the direction of the isobars. The wind does not blow directly from an area of high pressure to one of low pressure but is at an angle to the isobars, being directed across the isobars towards the lower pressure. In the northern hemisphere the wind circulates in an anticlockwise direction around a low pressure area and in a clockwise direction around a high pressure area.

Reference to figure 2 shows the wind, depicted by arrows, following this rule. Note how the wind blows slightly across the isobars towards the lower pressure. SSW winds are being experienced in the Irish Sea, with low pressure over southwest Ireland, and ESE winds over the North Sea, with the high pressure to the northeast over Scandinavia.

Figure 4 shows the way in which the wind arrows are drawn on a weather map. The small circle denotes the position of the reporting station and the arrows are seen to 'fly' with the wind. The feathers, always drawn on the side of the lowest pressure which, in the northern hemisphere, is on the right hand side when facing the wind, denote the wind strength.

The direction of the wind is always given from whence it is blowing since an observer is basically concerned with the type of weather that it is bringing with it. The strength of the wind is usually given, by and for seafarers, in the Beaufort notation, although it may be given directly as a speed in m.p.h. or knots.

The angle which the wind makes with the isobars is called the 'angle of indraft', see figure 4.

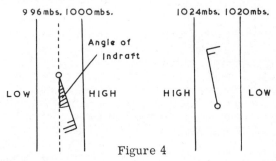

Figure 4

A further study of the weather map shows a clockwise shift in the wind direction between the eastern and western ends of the English Channel. The wind is said to 'veer' in this instance. When there is a shift of the wind in an anticlockwise direction the wind is said to 'back'. See figure 5.

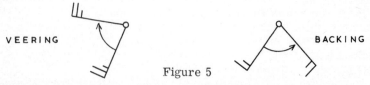

Figure 5

The symbols used for denoting the wind speed on a weather map, using the Beaufort notation, are shown on pages 104 and 105.

Variations in the direction and speed of the wind may be experienced over the land and close to the coast with the same pressure gradient. These variations occur between day and night and are brought about by the turbulent motion of the air near the ground. This turbulent motion is caused by the varying nature of the obstacles over which the air flows. The air is most turbulent during the hottest hours of the afternoon and it is then that the air attains its maximum speed, i.e. the wind strength is greatest.

Changes of up to 50 per cent in the wind strength are not uncommon over the land between daytime and nighttime with the same pressure gradient. The variations in the wind speed give rise to variations in the wind direction which might be as much as 30 degrees. These variations in the wind direction and strength are not normally experienced out to sea when well away from the coast.

Summarizing, the wind may be said to strengthen and veer by day, back and lull by night.

GUSTS AND SQUALLS

Gusts are changes in the wind speed lasting only a few seconds whereas squalls may last for some minutes. Gusts which are usually associated with squally weather may attain speeds of 60 knots and above.

Squalls may be caused by large temperature differences over a relatively short distance, a line squall is an example of this, see page 43 , or they may be caused by turbulence due to obstacles in the path of a moving air mass. Very strong gusts have resulted from the eddy currents set up in this way, with disastrous results.

TEMPERATURE

Although the reader will not have details of the temperature distribution when drawing a weather map, except for a possible general idea of the maximum and minimum temperatures to be reached over the British Isles, it is necessary to appreciate the changes that may occur between different places and to have an idea of the temperature distribution within the prevailing pressure system.

THE MEASUREMENT OF TEMPERATURE

Temperature is measured by means of a thermometer graduated in either degrees Celsius (Centigrade) or Fahrenheit. The Celsius scale is replacing the Fahrenheit scale in weather reports.

The conversion from one scale to another may be carried out in the following manner:-

(a)   Temp. $°C = (°F - 32°) \times \dfrac{5}{9}$ or, $°C = (°F + 40°) \times \dfrac{5}{9} - 40°$

(b)   Temp. $°F = (°C \times \dfrac{9}{5}) + 32°$ or, $°F = (°C + 40°) \times \dfrac{9}{5} - 40°$

Example: Convert (i) 54° F to °C
(ii) 17°C to °F

(i) Substituting in (a) above

Temp. $°C = (54° - 32°) \times \dfrac{5}{9} = 22° \times \dfrac{5}{9} = 12 \cdot 2°C.$

or, $°C = (54° + 40°) \times \dfrac{5}{9} - 40°$

$= 94° \times \dfrac{5}{9} - 40° = 52 \cdot 2° - 40° = 12 \cdot 2°C.$

(ii) Substituting in (b) above,

Temp. $°F = 17° \times \dfrac{9}{5} + 32° = 30 \cdot 6° + 32° = 62 \cdot 6° F.$

or, $°F = (17° + 40°) \times \dfrac{9}{5} - 40°$

$= 57° \times \dfrac{9}{5} - 40° = 102 \cdot 6° - 40° = 62 \cdot 6° F.$

THE DISTRIBUTION OF TEMPERATURE

There is usually a decrease in temperature as the latitude increases; temperatures along the south coast of England are normally higher than those recorded in Scotland. The temperature varies not only with latitude but with height, the season of the year, the prevailing wind, the amount of cloud present and the nature of the surface.

The sun is the only source from which the earth receives any heat, this radiant heat being absorbed by the surface thus raising its temperature. The extent to which this takes place depends on the nature of the surface.

Over the land this radiant heat is concentrated within a very shallow layer since the soil is a poor conductor of heat. A considerable rise in the temperature takes place within this layer and in time the air in contact with the surface becomes heated, expands and, with cooler air lying above the surface, rises. This results in fairly high temperatures being experienced over the land.

Over the sea conditions are different since the heat received from the sun is absorbed to a considerable depth and instead of this heat being concentrated over a shallow layer it is spread over a far greater volume. Since far more heat is required to raise the temperature of the water relatively low temperatures are therefore experienced over the sea.

Generally temperatures over the land are higher than those over the sea especially at places situated well inland. An onshore or sea breeze will be found to have a tempering influence on the temperatures along a coastal belt.

At night, especially when the sky is clear, the land rapidly loses its heat by radiation to space and extremely low temperatures may be experienced. This is most noticeable during the winter months when with the long winter nights prolonged cooling takes place. The sea surface, on the other hand, loses its heat gradually since the heat is being drawn up continuously from well below the surface and this gradual cooling results in only small variations between the day and night temperatures over the sea.

In addition to the horizontal variation in temperature there is a decrease in temperature with height. The rate at which the temperature decreases, called the 'lapse rate', plays an important part in the formation of cloud, rain, etc. An average rate of decrease in temperature is 3°F or 2°C per 1,000 ft. throughout the atmosphere though occasionally there is found to be an increase in temperature with height; this is called an 'inversion' of temperature.

WATER VAPOUR

The presence of water vapour in the atmosphere may give rise to the formation of cloud, rain etc. It is constantly changing in its amount, being increased by evaporation from the surface of the seas, rivers and lakes; and decreased by condensation in the form of cloud, rain and fog.

The maximum amount of water vapour that can be present at any one time depends on the temperature of the air. Air which contains the maximum amount appropriate to its temperature is said to be saturated. When the air is not saturated it is said to be dry, unsaturated or moist depending on the amount of water vapour present.

When unsaturated air is cooled the degree of saturation increases until a temperature is reached when the air becomes saturated. The temperature at which saturation takes place is called the 'dew point temperature'. Further cooling of the air results in the excess water vapour present condensing into minute water droplets. This condensation takes the form of cloud, fog and mist when it occurs above the surface, dew and hoar frost when it occurs on the surface.

Although the major properties of the atmosphere have been described in the order of pressure, wind, temperature and water vapour it should be noted that all the phenomena connected with the "weather" may be attributed to temperature or to be exact "heat".

Changes in the temperature affect the atmospheric pressure which in turn affects the direction and strength of the wind. The amount of water vapour present in the atmosphere depends on the air temperature. Temperature affects the rate of evaporation and condensation of the water vapour.

In the following pages it will be seen that the pressure systems and associated weather are all directly concerned with temperature and temperature variations.

3

PRESSURE SYSTEMS

In the previous chapter reference has been made to anticyclones and depressions, i.e. areas of high and low pressure. Figure 6 shows the main types of pressure systems that may be encountered, each system having its own particular pressure distribution, winds and associated weather. These pressure systems may follow rapidly one behind the other or a particular type may persist for a few days, or, as is the case with anticyclones, for longer periods of time. There is frequently an overlap between the weather associated with one system and that of another system.

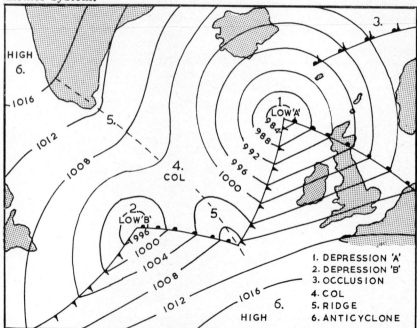

Figure 6

1. DEPRESSION 'A'
2. DEPRESSION 'B'
3. OCCLUSION
4. COL
5. RIDGE
6. ANTICYCLONE

AIR MASSES

An examination of a chart showing the temperature distribution over a large area will show large areas of warm and cold air, each covering many square miles in extent.

An air mass may be defined as a large mass of air covering an extensive area and having very little horizontal variation in any of its characteristics, especially temperature.

The boundaries between two different air masses are called ' frontal zones ' and the line where the frontal zone intersects the surface is called a ' front '.

Air masses originate in two main regions, these being the Poles and Tropics. Since the heating of the atmosphere is almost entirely by contact with the surface then a cold air mass will have been in contact with a cold surface and a warm air mass with a warm surface. The transfer of heat from the ground to the adjacent air mass is a slow process so that the air must have remained over the cold or warm regions for days or even weeks. The areas where this can take place are the slow moving regions of the polar and sub-tropical high pressure areas; such regions are known as 'source regions'.

Figure 7 shows the tracks of the various air masses found over the British Isles. The letters P, A and T denote the source regions of the air masses, namely 'polar', 'arctic' and 'tropical'. The small letters 'm' and 'c' denote the nature of the track which they will have followed since leaving the source region to their arrival over the British Isles, 'm' denoting a maritime track and 'c' a continental track.

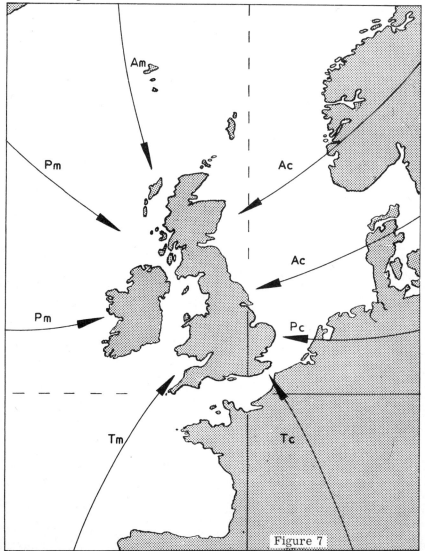

Figure 7

GENERAL CHARACTERISTICS OF AN AIR MASS

THE COLD AIR MASS

The main source is the Polar or Arctic Regions. At its source it is characterised by:-

    (1) low temperatures,

    (2) a low moisture content due to the low moisture capacity of the air at these very low temperatures,

    (3) a small change of temperature with height due to the intense cooling that has taken place in the lowest layers.

The tracks of all cold air masses are towards warmer regions and therefore the air in the lowest layers becomes warmed. The results of this heating are:-

    (i) the lapse rate increases in the lowest layers. Strong ascending currents of air develop (convection currents) when the cold air above overlies the warmer air at the surface;

    (ii) the moisture content of the air increases if the track lies over a warm ocean. The air temperature rises and thus its capacity to absorb moisture increases.

WARM AIR MASSES

These may initially be divided into two types, maritime and continental.

(a) Tropical Maritime Air Masses

Their main source region is the sub-tropical oceanic anticyclones. The high pressure area of the North Atlantic, or more locally in the vicinity of the Azores; the Azores High is a typical example. At their source they are characterised by:-

    (1) high temperatures derived from contact with a warm sea,

    (2) a high moisture content since there is an abundance of water vapour present,

    (3) a relatively small change of temperature with height.

The tracks of these air masses are towards higher latitudes and therefore the air becomes cooled in its lowest layers by contact with a cooler sea or land. This results in:-

    (i) the lapse rate in the lowest layers decreases still further;

    (ii) the cooling of the air in the lowest layers reduces the capacity of the air to absorb moisture and the dew point temperature is soon reached with saturation of the air.

(b) Tropical Continental Air Masses

Their main source region lies over North Africa. At the source they are characterised by:-

    (1) very high temperatures especially in their lowest layers,

    (2) a very low moisture content since the air is very dry.

The track of these air masses is towards higher latitudes and as they move northwards they become cooled in their lowest layers. The moisture content remains low unless they flow over the sea when, after a period of time, these types of air masses tend to change towards the maritime types.

TYPES OF WEATHER DUE TO DIFFERENT AIR MASSES

The distribution of the main atmospheric pressure systems strongly affects the pattern of the weather over the British Isles at different seasons of the year.

The main pressure systems involved are:-

    (a) The 'Icelandic' low pressure.   Occasionally this is replaced by an area of high pressure.

    (b) The 'Azores' high pressure.

    (c) The 'European' centre which is low in summer and high in winter.

Figure 8 shows the general distribution of these three main pressure systems in winter.

The essential features when considering the type of weather associated with a particular air mass are:-

    (1) the source region,

    (2) the changes that have taken place since leaving this region.

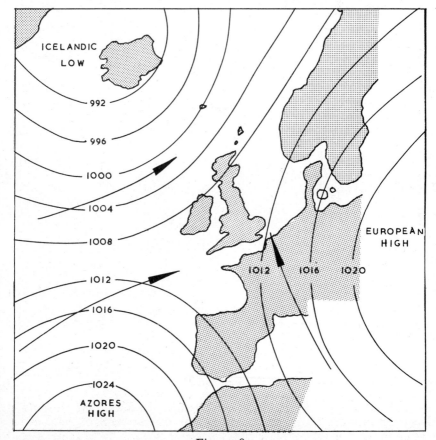

Figure 8

EXAMPLE 1

The General Synopsis

"A large depression is situated over Europe whilst an anticyclone is situated to the northwest of Ireland. A cold northerly air stream covers the British Isles ".

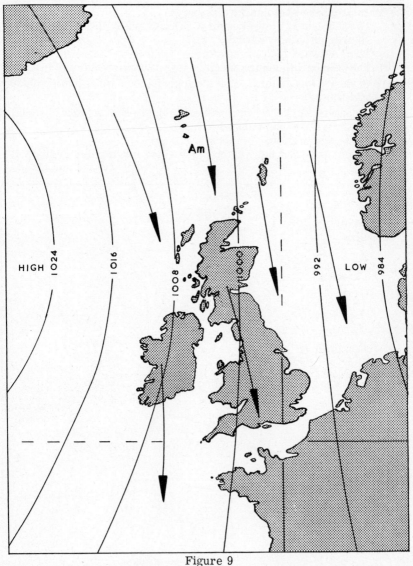

Figure 9

Figure 9 shows the pressure distribution and prevailing winds associated with the above general synopsis. The strength of the wind is given in the general forecast and is a useful guide to the spacing of the isobars, see page 108. The isobars lie in a north to south direction over the British Isles thus giving rise to northerly winds.

This type of air stream may be experienced during the winter, spring and summer when pressure remains high over Iceland and low over Europe. The air mass is of a Polar maritime (Pm) or Arctic (A) nature. The wind strengths are generally moderate to fresh but this will depend on the pressure gradient existing at the time and place.

Since this air mass is moving in a southerly direction the air in its lowest layers becomes heated. The warmer air absorbs vapour by direct evaporation from the sea and, with cold air above, strong convection currents are set up. The warm moist air cools on rising, its moisture content increases to saturation and a further rising of this air with resultant cooling gives rise to condensation of the excess water vapour and the formation of cloud.

Convection currents give rise to the formation of cumulus and cumulonimbus cloud.

'Cumulus' clouds are dense clouds with vertical development. The base of the cloud is nearly horizontal and the upper parts often resemble 'cauliflowers'. 'Cumulonimbus' clouds are heavy, dense clouds with considerable vertical development. They rise in the form of mountains and towers and the upper part often spreads out in the shape of an anvil, forming 'anvil cirrus', see figure 10.

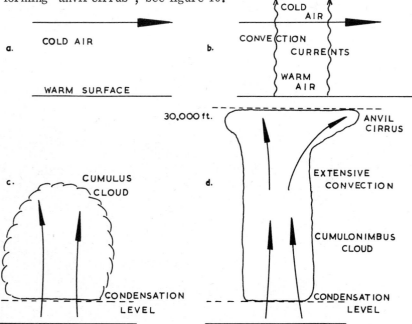

Figure 10.   The formation of cumulo cloud.

Precipitation will take the form of showers; snow during the winter, especially over high ground in the north, and rain during the spring and summer months. The showers, which may occur at any time of the day or night, will be frequent and heavy with the possibility of thunderstorms.

Temperatures will be relatively low and with clear skies at night frost is liable to occur in the winter and spring.

Visibility will be good except in the showers.

EXAMPLE 2

The General Synopsis
"Pressure remains high over Scandinavia and an easterly airstream covers the British Isles".

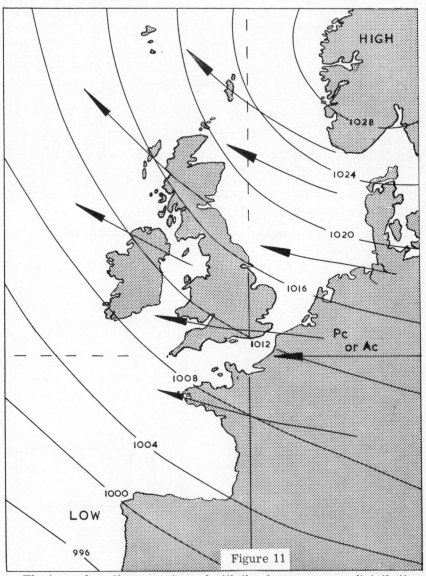

HIGH

1028

1024

1020

1016

Pc
or Ac

1012

1008

1004

1000

LOW

996

Figure 11

The type of weather experienced with the above pressure distribution and prevailing airstream depends on the time of the year. Marked differences in the weather are experienced between winter and summer.

Figure 11 shows the pressure distribution and the prevailing winds associated with the above synopsis. The air mass is of the Polar continental (Pc) or Arctic (Ac) type.

(a) In Winter

A steep pressure gradient gives rise to strong or gale force easterly winds over the whole of the British Isles.

Depressions moving in from the Atlantic are either stopped by this high pressure area or pass to the southeast of the area.

The cold dry winds leaving the continent are warmed and moistened as they cross the North Sea giving rise to convective currents and the formation of cumulus and cumulonimbus clouds near the east coast dying out as the air moves further inland away from the North Sea.

Should the air be subsiding within the anticyclone it will then warm and thus reduce the lapse rate above the surface. Instead of cumulus clouds developing there will then be the likelihood of low stratocumulus clouds due to turbulence.

Precipitation is in the form of rain or snow depending on the temperature prevailing. Most of the precipitation that takes place usually falls along the east coast although the south coast may experience precipitation when a depression moves eastwards up the English Channel.

Temperatures, especially during the winter, are very low and prolonged frost is a common occurrence.

Visibility is generally very good except in the rain or snow showers.

(b) In Summer

The pressure gradient is usually slack or weak giving rise to light to moderate easterly winds.

The polar air, warmed as it flows over a hot continent, is cooled as it crosses the North Sea. This cooling effect tends to give rise to stratus cloud along the east coast. The warm air cooled as it crosses the North Sea soon approaches saturation and a very little uplift, as may occur on striking the coast, will give the necessary cooling to bring about saturation, condensation and the formation of cloud. These clouds are of the stratus type, generally grey in colour and forming a uniform layer. They resemble fog but have their base above the surface, see figure 12.

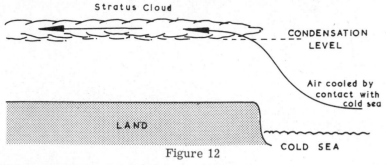

Figure 12

The possibility of precipitation is slight though light rain or drizzle may be experienced along the east coast of the British Isles.

Sea fog may form off the east coast if the temperature of the sea is sufficiently low to bring about the condensation of the water vapour in the lowest layers of the air. Mist or fog patches will therefore reduce visibility in this region.

Temperatures will generally be high but noticeable changes between day and night may be experienced.

EXAMPLE 3

The General Synopsis

" An anticyclone situated over Europe remains almost stationary with a weak depression out in the Atlantic to the west of Ireland. A southerly airstream covers the British Isles ".

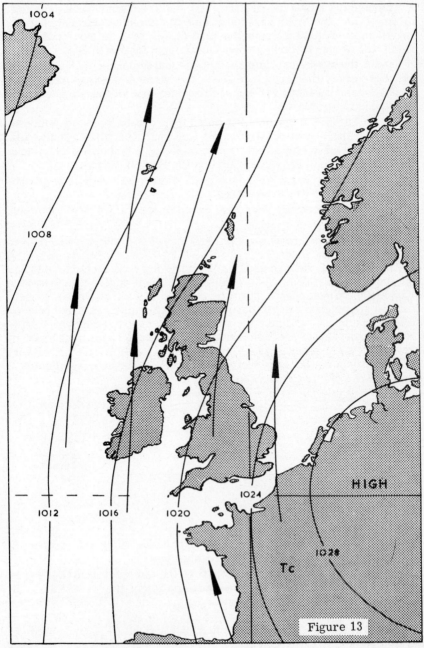

Figure 13

Figure 13 shows the weather map associated with the above synopsis. This type of pressure distribution occurs mainly during the summer months and the prevailing air stream is associated with a Tropical continental (Tc) air mass.

The pressure gradient is usually weak giving rise to light winds though the direction and strength of the wind experienced may be affected by localised conditions, i.e. land and sea breezes may occur along the coast, see page 89.

High temperatures and a low moisture content will give very little cloud since this type of air mass will have originated over a hot, dry continent.

The weather should remain dry and with very high temperatures prevailing there is the possibility of heat waves should this type of weather persist for any length of time.

Visibility is unlikely to be good, especially in the south of the region, since haze, due to dust being carried in from the continent, is likely.

When this type of air mass has been in contact with a sea surface it tends to have the characteristics of a Tropical maritime air mass, see example 4.

EXAMPLE 4

The General Synopsis

"A ridge of high pressure extends northeast from the Azores. A south-westerly air stream covers the British Isles".

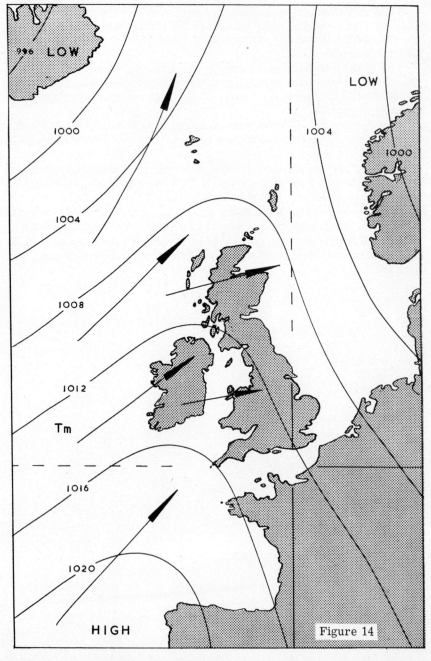

Figure 14

Figure 14 shows the weather map associated with the above synopsis. This type of weather may occur at all seasons of the year and is due to an extension to the northeast of the Azores high pressure area into the British Isles and Continent. The air mass associated with a pressure distribution of this nature is usually of a Tropical maritime (Tm) nature.

The winds are generally light to moderate, freshening towards the western sides of the British Isles as the depressions moving in from the North Atlantic are arrested or pass to the northwest of the area between Iceland and N.W. Scotland.

The weather is similar in winter and summer but the effect of solar heating is to change certain aspects.

(a) In Winter

The warm moist air of the tropics is cooled in its lowest layers as it moves northeast over the Atlantic towards Europe. This cooling, plus a high moisture content, soon brings about saturation with the formation of low lying stratus and stratocumulus cloud.

Stratocumulus cloud is a layer type cloud which is grey or whitish in colour with dark parts and composed of rounded masses, rolls etc., in lines or waves. When the whole sky is completely covered with this type of cloud it has a wavy appearance.

Orographic uplift, namely the air being forced to ascend on reaching the coast or high land, accelerates this cloud formation, see figure 12.

This surface cooling with the formation of cloud gives rise to light rain or drizzle which is heavier to the south and west of the area than elsewhere.

Temperatures are relatively high, and warm muggy days may be experienced.

At sea the cooling of this warm air by contact with a relatively cold sea surface will, providing the air is brought below its dew point temperature, give rise to the formation of sea fog. The areas most susceptible to the formation of sea fog are the Irish Sea, S.W. approaches to the British Isles and the English Channel.

(b) In Summer

Cloud amounts along the coastal regions are similar to those experienced in winter but inland and to the east of the British Isles the daytime heating soon disperses any stratiform cloud that may have formed during the night though it may reform or, if undispersed, thicken after sunset.

At night, well inland, there is the possibility of radiation fog forming but this will soon clear after sunrise. Radiation fog is due to the land cooling by the radiation of heat from the earth's surface with a clear sky at night. The subsequent cooling of the moist air in contact with the ground, to and below its dew point temperature, brings about condensation and the formation of fog.

EXAMPLE 5

The General Synopsis

"A deep depression situated to the north of Scotland remains almost stationary giving rise to a strong westerly air stream over the British Isles".

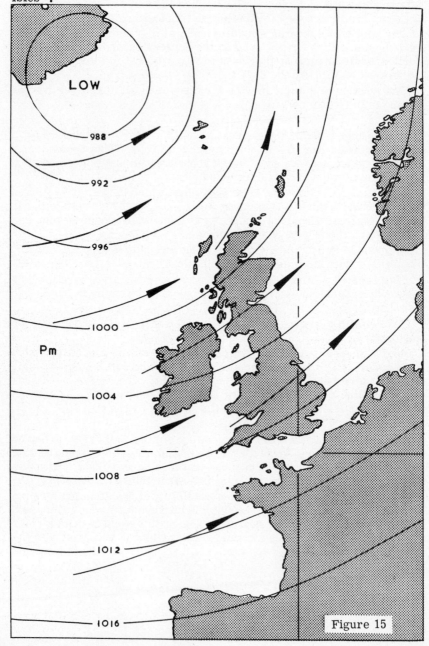

Figure 15

Figure 15 shows the weather map associated with the above pressure distribution. This type of pressure pattern may occur at all times of the year, the whole region lying under the influence of this deep depression to the north of Scotland.

The associated air mass is of a Polar maritime (Pm) nature and differs from that of example 1 due to the fact that the air mass has been in contact with the sea for a greater period of time since leaving its source region.

Similar weather conditions prevail during winter and summer though differences are experienced due to the differing amounts of solar radiation received.

(a) In Winter

The deep depression with a very low pressure at its centre and a steep pressure gradient will give rise to fresh, strong and even gale force winds. The strength of the wind decreases away from the centre of the depression so that gale force winds may be expected around Scotland and the north of England decreasing in strength towards the south. The Irish Sea and Western Approaches to the British Isles will experience strong to gale force winds with fresh to strong winds in the North Sea and English Channel.

Since the air mass is of a Polar maritime origin the air in the lowest layer will have been heated by contact with a relatively warm sea surface thus raising the temperature and moisture content of this layer. Cold air overlying this warmer air will give rise to convective currents and the formation of cumulus and cumulonimbus clouds, especially over the open sea and windward coasts. Along the south coast there is the possibility of shallow cloud layers forming, i.e. stratus.

Precipitation will take the form of showers, being heaviest in the north of the region and decreasing towards the south. If temperatures are sufficiently low these showers will be of snow especially over high ground to the north.

Along the eastern side of the region and to leeward of high ground, also in areas sheltered from the strong winds, cooling by radiation at night may give rise to the formation of fog and frost.

(b) In Summer

Over the open sea and along the west coast, i.e. on windward coasts, the weather is similar to that experienced in winter. Strong winds, convective clouds with frequent rain showers and below average temperatures.

Inland and especially to the south and east of the British Isles high temperatures by day will give rise to strong convective currents and the formation of cumulus and cumulonimbus cloud. Frequent rain showers may occur with the possibility of thunderstorms.

FRONTAL DEPRESSIONS

These are the result of an interaction between two different air masses, i.e. a polar and a tropical air mass. An examination of the major high and low pressure areas of the North Atlantic shows a sub-tropical area of high pressure and a polar area of high pressure with a belt of low pressure lying between them. The sub-tropical high gives rise to a belt of westerly winds across the North Atlantic to the north of latitude 40° N. Much further to the north under the influence of the polar high the winds are generally from an easterly direction, see figure 16.

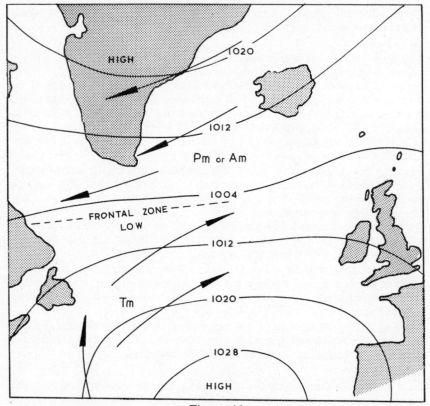

Figure 16

When pressure is low over Greenland the westerly air flow across the North Atlantic is accentuated, a frequent occurrence during the winter months, and the polar winds from the north and the tropical winds from the south flow side by side with a 'frontal zone' lying between them. Figure 17 shows the above pressure distribution.

The frontal zone, between the polar winds from the north and the tropical winds from the south, gives rise to a line of discontinuity and it is along this line that the depressions are liable to form.

The majority of depressions that affect the British Isles form over on the western side of the North Atlantic and are then carried across the ocean in the general westerly air stream.

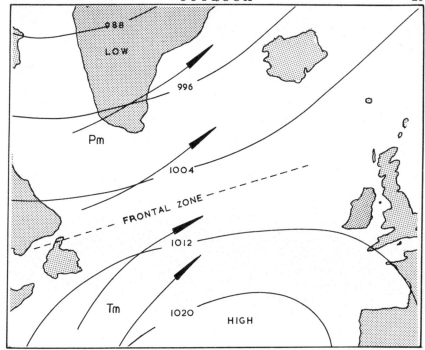

Figure 17

In order to understand the weather associated with frontal depressions it is necessary to have a brief outline of their formation, growth and decay.

A 'front' is the intersection of a frontal zone with the surface; the frontal zone being the boundary between two adjacent air masses. The particular property used to distinguish an air mass, namely its temperature, is also used to distinguish fronts. Since air masses are generally in motion the fronts will also be in motion. A front moving in such a manner that cold air is replacing warm air at the surface is called a 'cold front' and when warm air replaces cold air at the surface it is known as a 'warm front'. Figure 18 shows how the various fronts are depicted on a weather map.

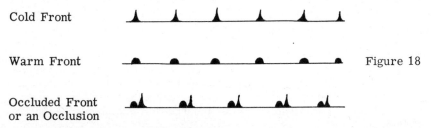

Cold Front

Warm Front   Figure 18

Occluded Front
or an Occlusion

The sequence of events that takes place during the life cycle of a frontal depression is shown in figures 19 to 28. Depressions may be looked upon as disturbances in the general westerly air flow across the North Atlantic.

THE LIFE CYCLE OF A DEPRESSION

(1)   Initially the warm and cold air masses flow side by side, either in the same or in opposite directions. There has to be a relative motion between, and convergence of, the two air masses. Figure 19 shows the tropical air mass flowing from a W.S.W'ly direction and the polar air mass flowing from an E.N.E'ly direction towards the area of low pressure. This convergence is also shown in figures 16 and 17.

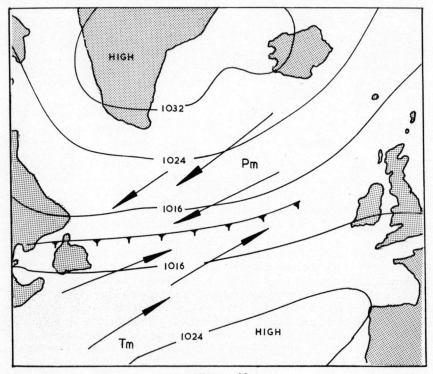

Figure 19

(2)   The frontal zone between the two air masses is not vertical but is inclined at an angle such that the warmer, less dense air is overlying the colder, denser air. Figure 20 shows a cross section through the frontal zone. The front at the surface is shown on a weather map as a cold front since the colder air is undercutting and advancing on the warmer air.

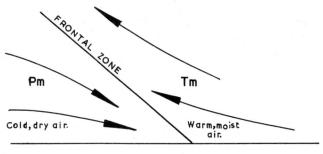

Figure 20

(3)   When a tongue of warm air pushes northwards and overrides still further the cold air a further reduction in the barometric pressure takes place and a definite low pressure area is established, Low 'A'.   The low continues to deepen, i.e. pressure falls at the centre, and warm and cold fronts are set up, see figure 21.

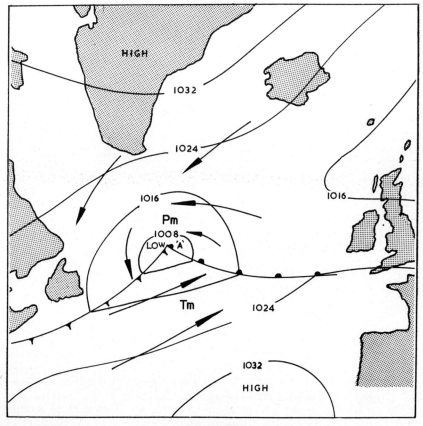

Figure 21

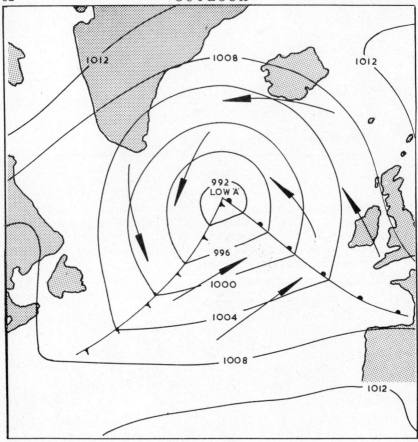

Figure 22

(4) Figure 22 shows Low 'A' fully established, taking on the familiar pattern of a frontal depression. The area between the warm and cold fronts is called the 'warm sector' of the depression.

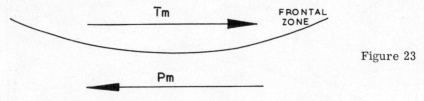

Figure 23

(5) Figure 23 shows a cross section through a frontal depression to the north of the centre, i.e. on the polar side. The tongue of warm air aloft is seen moving in the opposite direction to the cold air at the surface.

(6) Figure 24 shows a cross section to the south of the centre, i.e. on the equatorial side. At the warm front the air is seen to be sliding up or overriding the colder air whereas at the cold front the cold air is advancing on the warm air, undercutting it and lifting it off the surface.

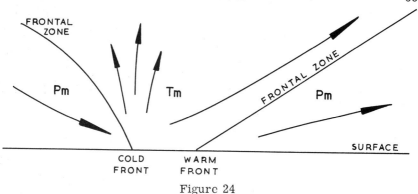

Figure 24

(7) Since the warm front advances at a slower rate than the cold front the area of the warm sector decreases as the cold front catches up with the warm front, (figure 25). Low 'A' is now situated to the south of Iceland with the fronts lying to the west of the British Isles.

A second depression, Low 'B', has now formed out in the Atlantic on the trailing edge of the cold front of Low 'A'.

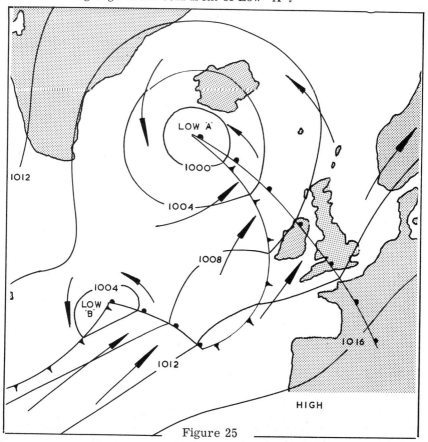

Figure 25

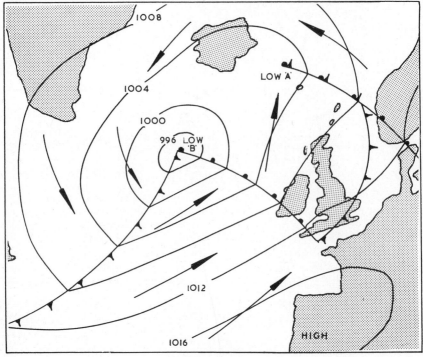

Figure 26

(8)   The cold front finally advances and catches up with the warm front, the process normally commencing at the centre of the depression. When this takes place the fronts are said to occlude. The depression at this stage usually starts to fill up since the warm sector slowly disappears, see figure 26.   Low 'A' is now to the north of the British Isles.

(9)   Figure 27 shows a cross section through an occluded front. The cold air in the rear of the cold front has now 'caught up' with the cold air before the warm front. Cold air replaces the warm air at the surface.

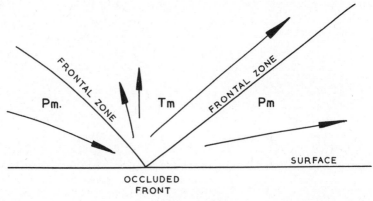

Figure 27

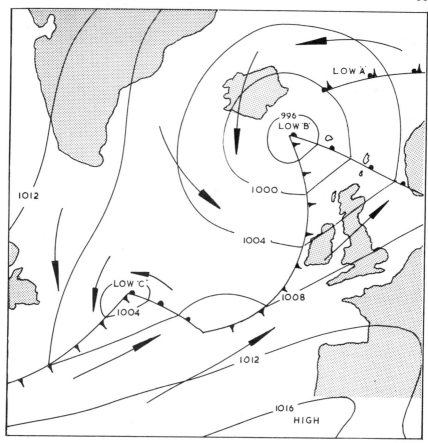

Figure 28

(10)   Figure 28 shows Low 'A' completely occluded to the northeast of the British Isles. Low 'B' has now become fully established and has taken the place of Low 'A'. Out in the Atlantic another depression, Low 'C', has formed on the trailing edge of Low 'B's cold front, a new depression in the family.

Depressions tend to run in 'families', a number of depressions following one upon the other, each new depression forming on the trailing cold front of its predecessor.

The whole system, depressions and fronts, usually travels in a north-easterly to easterly direction across the North Atlantic at speeds up to 25 knots, although there is a tendency for them to slow down on approaching the British Isles.

The following examples show the type of weather associated with the passage of a frontal depression. The first example shows a depression with its centre to the north of the British Isles, warm and cold fronts passing successively over the region, and the second example shows the depression passing to the south of the region.

EXAMPLE 6

The General Synopsis

"A depression situated to the south of Iceland is moving slowly east and its associated fronts are moving eastwards towards the British Isles. The fronts are expected to clear most areas within the next 24 hours to be followed by a showery westerly airstream".

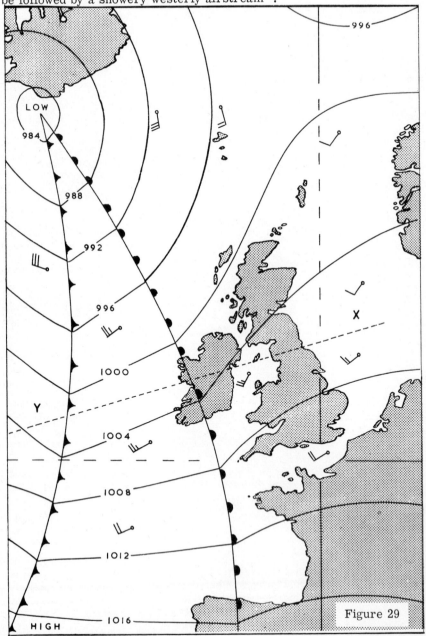

Figure 29

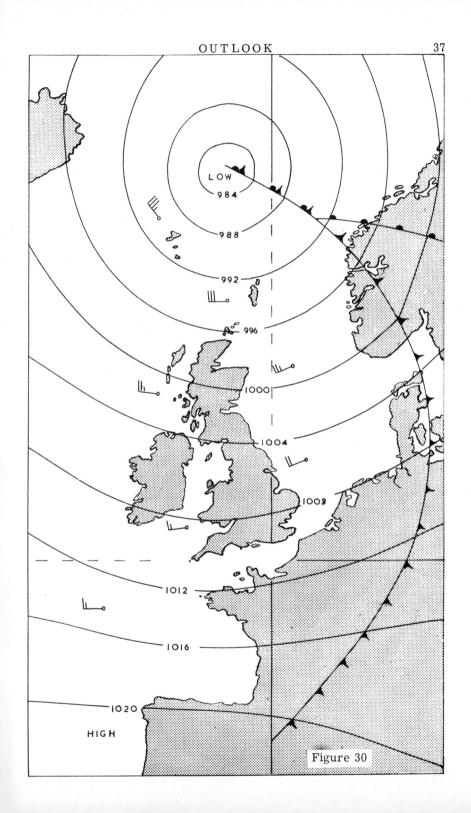

LOW
984
988
992
996
1000
1004
1008
1012
1016
1020
HIGH

Figure 30

Figure 29 shows the general pressure distribution, wind direction and strength and the position of the fronts at the time of the above synopsis. The warm front is seen to run in a NNW to SSE direction from the south of Iceland to the Bay of Biscay with the cold front lying to the west of Ireland.

Figure 30 shows the pressure distribution 24 hours later. The centre of the depression now lies to the east of Iceland and the fronts have completely cleared the British Isles and North Sea. A westerly air stream now covers the British Isles.

Figure 31 shows a cross section through the depression, to the south of the centre, along the line XY, and will help the reader to understand the type of weather that may be experienced. It shows the vertical movement of the air at the fronts and is a more detailed figure than that shown in figure 24, page 33. At the warm front the warm moist air (Tm) is overriding or sliding up over the colder air (Pm) at the surface and at the cold front the cold air is seen to be undercutting and replacing the warm surface air.

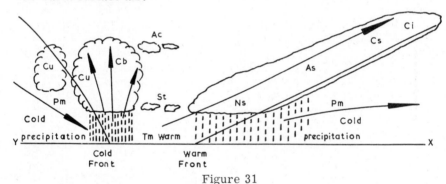

Figure 31

The following sequence describes the weather, pressure and winds associated with the passage of the fronts.

The air rising at the warm front cools, becomes saturated and condensation takes place with the formation of cloud. Well ahead of this front the air has risen to a height of possibly 25,000 feet or more thus giving rise to the formation of high clouds.

An observer, at position X for instance in the North Sea, will see these high clouds approaching from the west. As the warm front approaches the cloud amount will increase and its base will decrease in height as the lower cloud types cover the sky, see figure 31. The cloud sequence is frequently Cirrus, giving way to Cirrostratus, Altostratus and finally Nimbostratus. These clouds may be described as follows:-

Cirrus: (Ci.)	detached clouds in the form of white delicate filaments or narrow bands of clouds. They often resemble mares tails. They have a fibrous appearance with a height above 18,000 feet.
Cirrostratus: (Cs.)	a transparent whitish cloud which forms a veil over the sky and has a fibrous or smooth appearance with a height above 18,000 feet.

Altostratus: a greyish or bluish cloud sheet which covers the sky
(As.)   and through which the sun vaguely shows. The height
                 is between 8,000 and 18,000 feet.

Nimbostratus: a grey cloud, often dark, from which precipitation takes
(Ns.)   place. It is thick enough to completely obscure the sun.
                 A low cloud having a height from just above the surface
                 to about 8,000 feet.

Pressure will fall as the warm front approaches, the wind strengthening and veering towards the SW. Tracing a path along the line XY the pressure is seen to fall from approximately 1006 mbs. to 1002 mbs, and with an increase in the pressure gradient the wind strengthens accordingly.

Precipitation, drizzle turning to rain, will set in with the approach of the altostratus cloud and will then be more or less continuous until the passage of the front. Visibility will deteriorate due to the precipitation.

Temperatures will remain fairly steady and will not show any noticeable increase until the warmer air is met with on the passage of the warm front.

As the warm front passes over the observer precipitation will rapidly decrease with the possibility of clearing skies. The temperature will rise and with the cessation of precipitation visibility will improve.

The pressure, which had been falling, will now remain fairly steady, and the wind will be blowing in a steady direction from the SW.

Occasionally the sky is covered by stratus cloud and drizzle or fog may occur. When the surface temperature (land or sea) is below the dew point temperature of the air, condensation will result with the formation of drizzle, mist or fog. Fog in the Irish Sea, English Channel and S.W. approaches to the British Isles is frequently caused in this way.

At the cold front strong convection currents are set up as the cold air undercuts the warm air. Cumulus and cumulonimbus clouds are formed giving rise to heavy showers. Ahead of the cold front altocumulus clouds may be observed.

Altocumulus: a white or grey cloud layer generally having shadows.
(Ac.)   They are frequently of a wavy appearance or composed
                 of rounded masses, rolls etc. Their height is between
                 8,000 and 18,000 feet.

Pressure will rise quickly with the passage of the cold front as the cold, dense air (Pm) replaces the warm air at the surface. The wind will veer sharply to the west, even to the NW for a time, increasing in strength with occasional strong gusts.

Precipitation from the convective clouds will be heavy with the possibility of thunderstorms. Visibility will be poor in the showers but good elsewhere.

As the cold front moves away to the east the sky will clear and cumulus clouds will form within the westerly air stream. The barometer will continue to rise, the wind being from a west to NW'ly direction. Showery weather may be expected, the distribution of pressure and the type of weather being similar to that of example 5, page 26.

EXAMPLE 7

The General Synopsis
"A depression situated to the southwest of the British Isles is expected to move northeast and deepen".

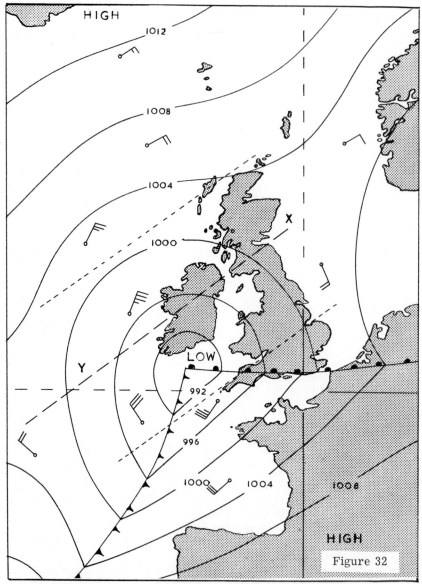

Figure 32

Figure 32 shows the pressure distribution, direction and strength of the wind and the position of the fronts at the time of the above synopsis.

Figure 33 shows the pressure distribution etc., approximately 24 hours later with the centre of the depression situated over the North Sea.

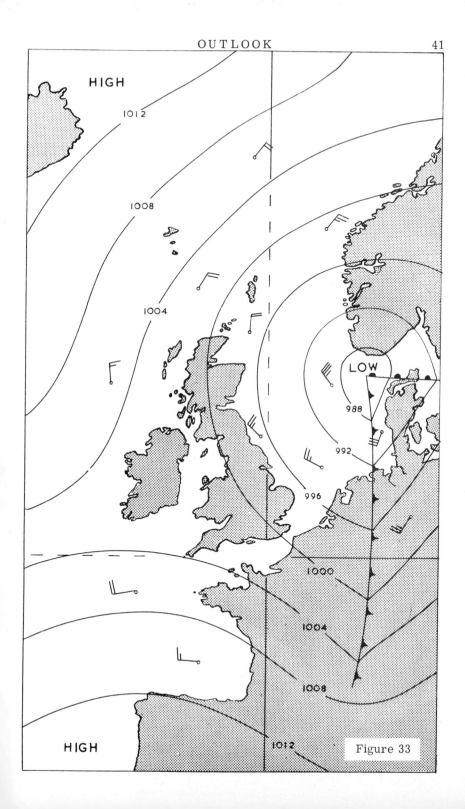

Figure 33

The pressure is falling at and around the centre of the depression as it deepens and as the pressure falls the pressure gradient will possibly steepen thus giving increased wind strengths in most areas.

The weather likely to be experienced by an observer will depend on his position relative to the central low. The region to be covered by the forecast has been divided into three sections, as depicted by the dotted lines, which are as follows:-

(1) an area to the south of the centre,
(2) an area immediately to the north of the centre, and
(3) an area covering the northern part of the region, clear of the centre.

The forecast area by area is as follows:-

(1)   To the south of the depression, in the area influenced by the fronts, the weather will follow a similar pattern to that described in the previous example.

A noticeable veer in the wind direction will be experienced at the fronts as shown by the abrupt change in the direction of the isobars along the fronts. Frontal activity will increase as the depression deepens and with a steepening pressure gradient strong to gale force winds may be experienced within this region. S'ly gales veering to SW and possibly NW may be experienced along the south coast of England and in the English Channel.

(2)   To the north of the centre there are no fronts at the surface since the warm air is overlying the cold surface air. Figure 34 shows a cross section through this part of the depression along the line XY.

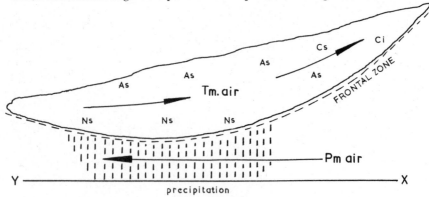

Figure 34

The pressure will decrease as the centre approaches and passes to the south of the observer and will then commence to rise. The wind direction, initially from the south, will back through east and north to northwest with the passage of the depression and with the pressure gradient steepening towards the centre, plus a general deepening of the depression, the wind strengths will be increased.

The warm air extending to the north and northeast of the centre, over-riding the colder air at the surface, will give rise initially to cirrus, then cirrostratus (possibly merging to give cirrocumulus), altostratus and nimbostratus cloud, see figure 34 and page 32.

Cirrocumulus: This is a layer of high cloud having a globular appear-
(Cc.)   ance arranged in groups or lines, or more often in
                ripples, and is popularly known as a "mackerel sky".

Precipitation will set in as the lower clouds, altostratus and nimbostratus, approach and will be heaviest near the centre with the possibility
of thunderstorms as the centre passes and the barometer starts to rise.
Visibility, generally poor, will depend on the amount of precipitation.

(3)   To the north of the region the weather will be similar to that
experienced with an easterly airstream off the continent. The air mass
will be of a Pc or Ac nature, see example 2, page 20.

Cloud amounts will decrease as the distance from the centre of the
depression increases. Since the high cirrus and cirrostratus clouds
extend well ahead and to the north of the depression there may still be
extensive cloud coverage but only a slight possibility of precipitation.

A LINE SQUALL

When a cold front is well defined the sudden undercutting of the warm
air by the advancing colder air may give rise to cumulonimbus clouds,
heavy rain, thunderstorms and squally weather.

A noticeable drop in the air temperature and a rapid rise in the
pressure takes place as the warm air is replaced by the colder air at
the front. Frequently the cold air aloft overruns the surface cold air,
figure 35, due to frictional drag at the surface. The tip of the advancing
cold air, having a tendency to fall, imparts a rolling motion to the cloud
and a low black roll cloud is often seen to precede the front.

With the passage of the front a marked veer in the wind direction
takes place as is shown by the wind arrows in figure 35.

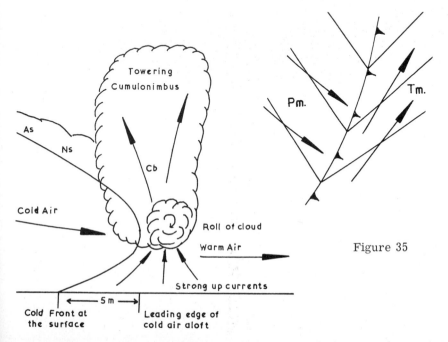

Figure 35

SECONDARY DEPRESSIONS

Small depressions which form within the circulation of a larger depression are called 'secondary depressions'. They form on the equatorial side of the larger depressions and tend to be carried around this depression in an anti-clockwise direction, (northern hemisphere), being carried along by the main circulation.

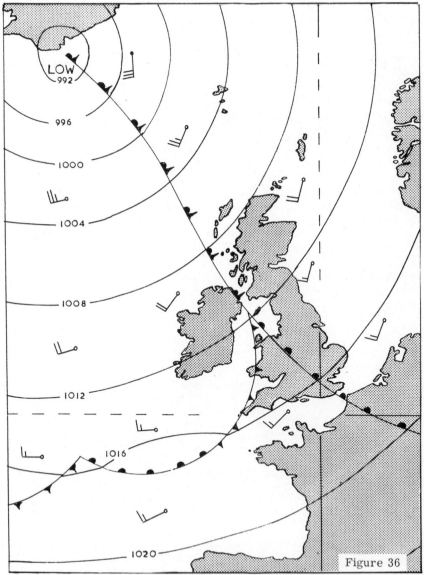

Figure 36

Secondaries frequently form on the trailing edge of the cold front of an occluding depression. A depression forming well outside the primary circulation becomes the next member in the family of depressions. Figures 36, 37, 38 and 39 illustrate the formation of a secondary depression.

(1) The first indication of a secondary forming may be nothing more than just a small wave or kink in the isobars, figure 36.

(2) The wave then deepens, warm and cold fronts are set up, and the secondary depression becomes established, figure 37.

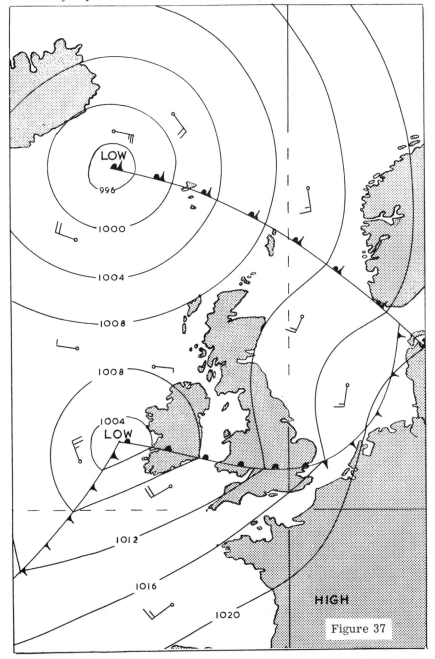

Figure 37

(3) The secondary, now established, may continue to deepen and with the primary depression occluding it may grow in size and finally take over from the primary depression, figure 38.

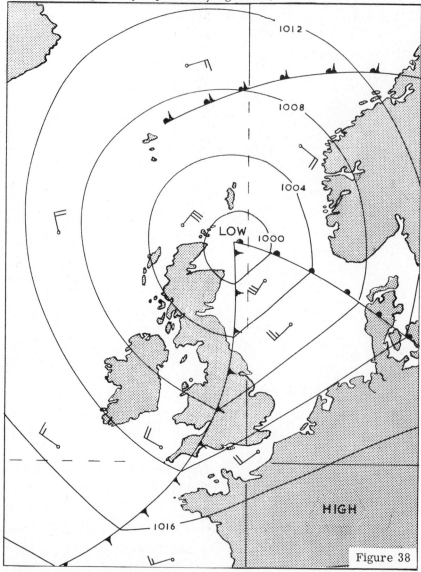

Figure 38

A secondary may also form at the top of a warm sector which is partly occluded. The formation of a secondary by this method is not a frequent occurrence and usually requires the depression to be slowed by a mountain barrier, i.e. Scandinavia, so that the secondary breaks away to the south of the obstruction, figure 39.

Other small secondary disturbances of a localised nature may be caused by local heating or orographical features.

Secondary Depression forming at the tip of the warm sector of
a partly occluded depression

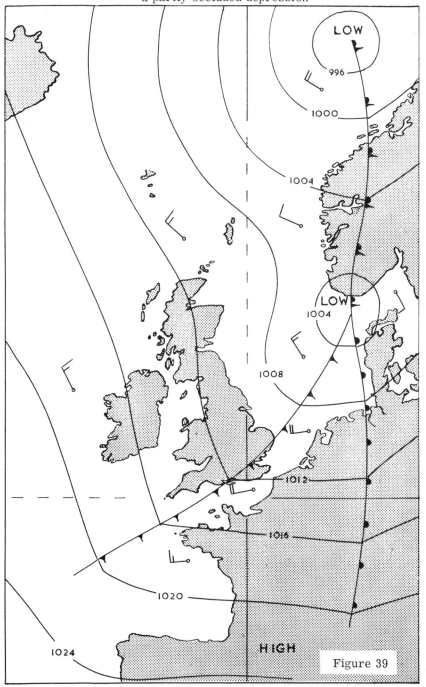

Figure 39

THE WEATHER OF A SECONDARY

Secondaries generally form within a large occluded or inactive depression which may be giving rise to very little bad weather. Secondaries may cause cloud and rain, thunderstorms being frequent during the summer. The strongest winds experienced within a secondary are on the side furthest from the primary depression since the circulation of the secondary intensifies that of the primary. Between the two centres of low pressure calms and light winds are usually experienced.

EXAMPLE 8

The General Synopsis

"A depression situated to the northeast of Scotland is expected to fill whilst a secondary depression situated to the southwest of Ireland is expected to move eastwards into the North Sea during the next 24 hours and will affect all areas".

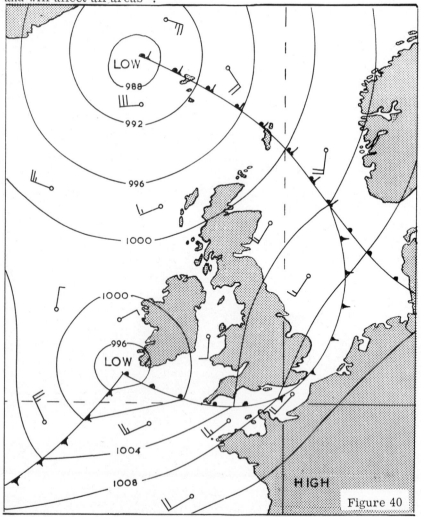

Figure 40

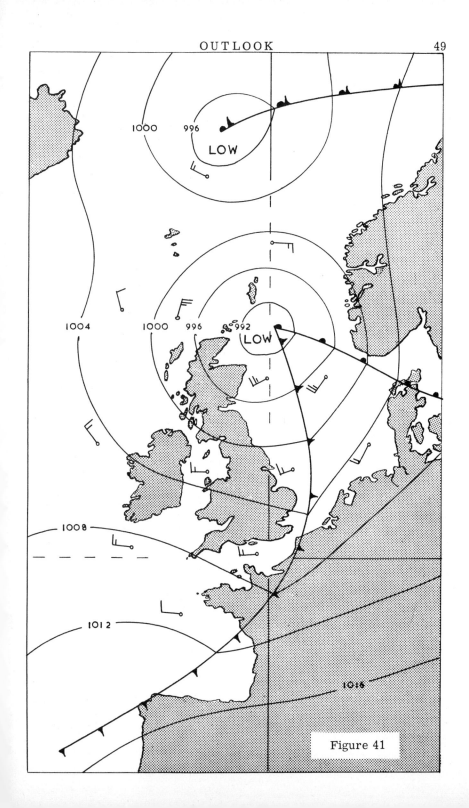

Figure 41

Figure 40 shows the pressure distribution and prevailing winds for the above synopsis. Between the low to the northeast of Scotland and the secondary low southwest of Ireland there is a weak ridge of high pressure which is at present affecting eastern parts of the British Isles.

The secondary depression will be the predominating pressure system to affect the British Isles and adjacent sea areas since the low pressure to the northeast of Scotland is expected to fill. This secondary is typical of the type shown in figure 36, page 44.

Figure 41 shows the pressure distribution and prevailing winds 24 hours later with the secondary now well established, the central low being situated over the North Sea, the cold front having cleared all regions of the British Isles.

The type of weather associated with the above synopsis is similar to that of examples 6 and 7 but probably to a lesser degree. The sequence of weather observed will depend on the observer's position relative to the centre of the secondary.

In the rear of the cold front strong to gale force winds may be experienced as here the circulation of the secondary intensifies the circulation around the original depression. Calm, light variable winds may be experienced between the two centres, to the west of Scotland. Such a region is referred to as a Col, see page 71.

A General Forecast for the above would be:-
Cloud and rain will spread across most of England during the next 24 hours to be followed by brighter, showery weather from the west. Scotland will be partly cloudy with scattered showers.

TROUGHS OF LOW PRESSURE

Troughs of low pressure, indicated by isobars extending outwards from a region of low pressure, have the lower pressure along the line of the trough. The isobars frequently change sharply in direction at the trough forming a 'V' shape.

Troughs of low pressure, especially when there is a marked change in the direction of the isobars, may be associated with warm, cold or occluded fronts. The sequence of weather associated with the passage of warm and cold fronts has been described in example 6, page 36.

An occluded front is one where the cold front has finally overtaken the warm front at the surface. The warm sector decreases in area until finally there is no longer any warm air at the surface. The occluding of a depression commences at the centre working outwards, as shown on page 34, and when complete the depression is said to be occluded and the front on the weather map is called an occlusion, figure 42.

Many of the depressions which affect the British Isles are partly occluded as will be seen from the various weather maps drawn in the figures here or as are depicted on the television and in the press.

If the air before the warm front was identical to that in the rear of the cold front all identity would then be lost along the line of an occlusion and no front would be shown on a weather map. Invariably there is a difference between these two air masses, one being colder than the other.

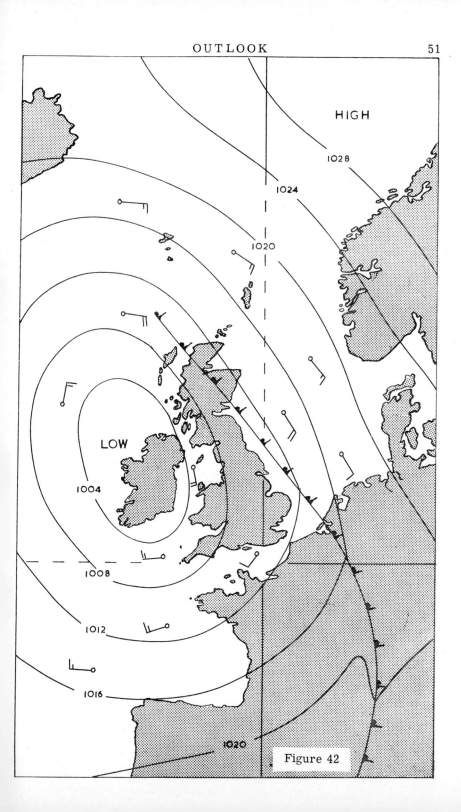

Figure 42

The type of weather associated with an occlusion varies considerably and may be of the warm front or cold front type, or, as the depression fills and slowly disappears nothing more than cloud may mark its passage.

Warm Occlusion

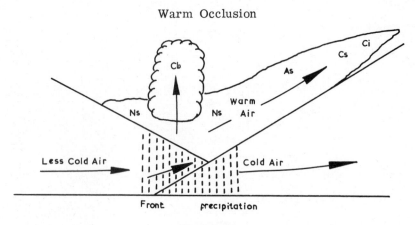

Figure 43

Figure 43 shows the type of weather associated with an occlusion where the air in the rear of the occluded front is warmer than that in advance of the front and figure 44 shows the weather to be expected when the air in the rear of the occluded front is colder than that ahead of it. These are referred to as warm and cold occlusions respectively. As will be seen from these cross sections a combination of warm and cold front weather may be expected with a tendency for one or the other to predominate.

Cold Occlusion

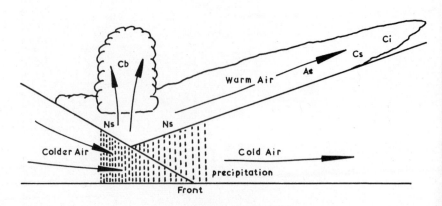

Figure 44

EXAMPLE 9

The General Synopsis

"A deep depression is situated to the south of Iceland with its associated trough to the west of Ireland. The trough is expected to move slowly eastwards across the British Isles during the next 24 hours ".

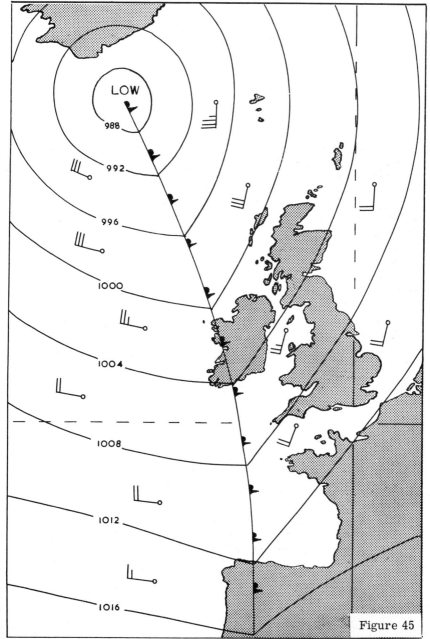

Figure 45

Figure 45 shows the general pressure distribution for the above synopsis. The trough of low pressure, an occluded front, extends south from Iceland to the Bay of Biscay. Figure 46 shows the probable pressure distribution 24 hours later when the trough has cleared the British Isles. The centre of the depression is shown to the east of Iceland and its associated trough lies in a southeasterly direction to the southwest of Scandinavia.

The rate at which a front moves is governed by the wind strength in the rear of the front. Notice that the isobars are V-shaped at the front.

The type of weather associated with a trough depends on whether the occlusion is of the warm or cold front type. Since the occluded front is associated with a deep depression it is probable that the occlusion is relatively new in which case warm front weather will be followed by cold front weather.

An observer to the east of the front will possibly experience the following sequence of weather.

High clouds, cirrus, well ahead of the front will be followed by cirro-stratus, altostratus and nimbostratus as the trough approaches. Precipitation will set in which will be moderately heavy and continuous. The pressure will fall quite rapidly and the wind will be steady in direction from the SW, increasing in strength as the front approaches.

At the occluded front, as the cold air is met at the surface. heavy showers, even thunderstorms, may be experienced, associated with cumulonimbus clouds, in addition to the nimbostratus already present.

The pressure, falling to the trough, will now rise rapidly, the wind veering sharply to the NW and strengthening with the possibility of gusts of gale force and above.

In the rear of the trough line the overcast will clear giving blue skies and broken cloud, cumulus, as may be experienced with a NW'ly air stream. Showers with sunny periods may then be expected, see example 5 page 26.

A General Forecast for the above would be:-

Most places will have cloudy weather and the rain in the west will slowly spread to most eastern regions. Sunny intervals are likely in Ireland and the west of England as the trough crosses the region. The outlook will be dull with rain at first in the east, otherwise showers and sunny periods .

Figures 47 and 48 show two other occasions when troughs of low pressure may be reported in the general synopsis. Figure 47 shows a warm front and figure 48 a cold front with figure 49 showing the pressure distribution and prevailing winds after both fronts have cleared the British Isles. The type of weather experienced will be that normally associated with the respective fronts, i.e. warm or cold front weather, see example 6 page 36.

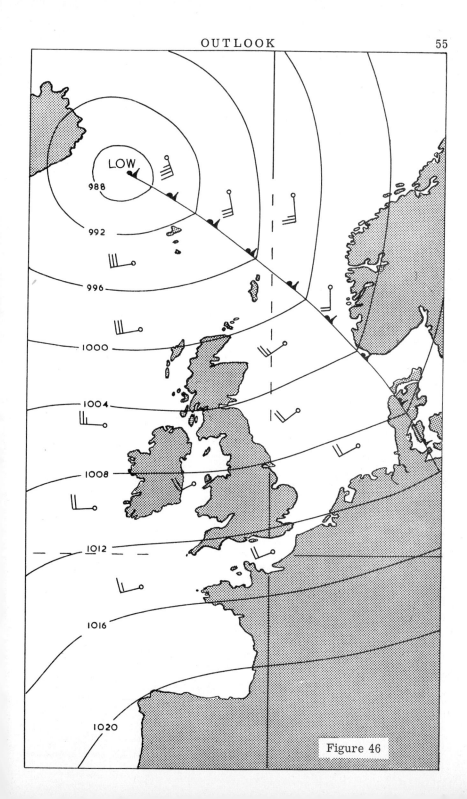

Figure 46

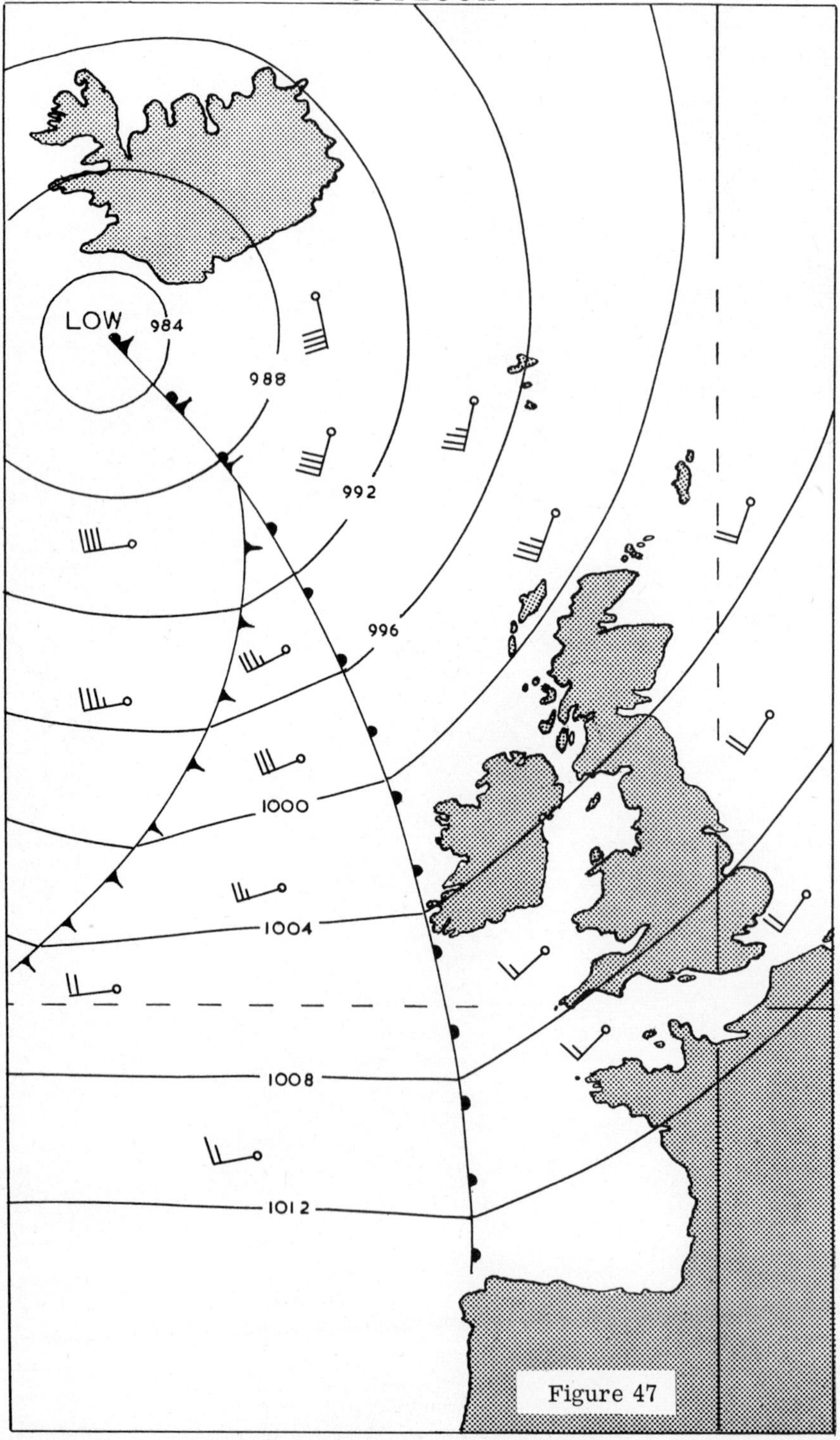

LOW 984
988
992
996
1000
1004
1008
1012

Figure 47

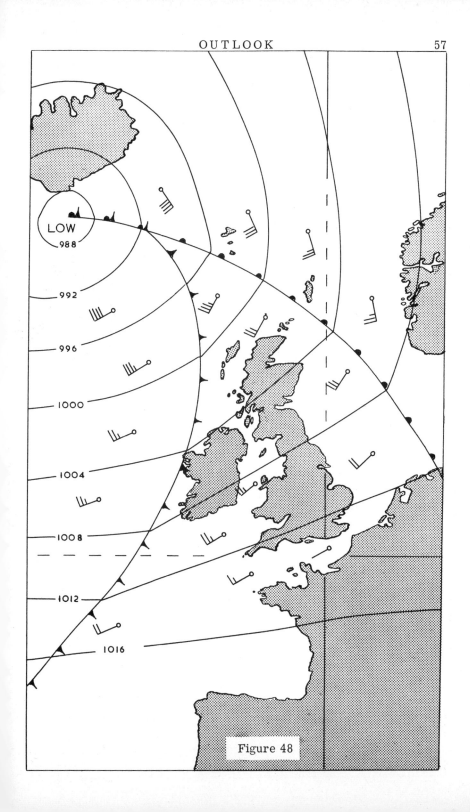

Figure 48

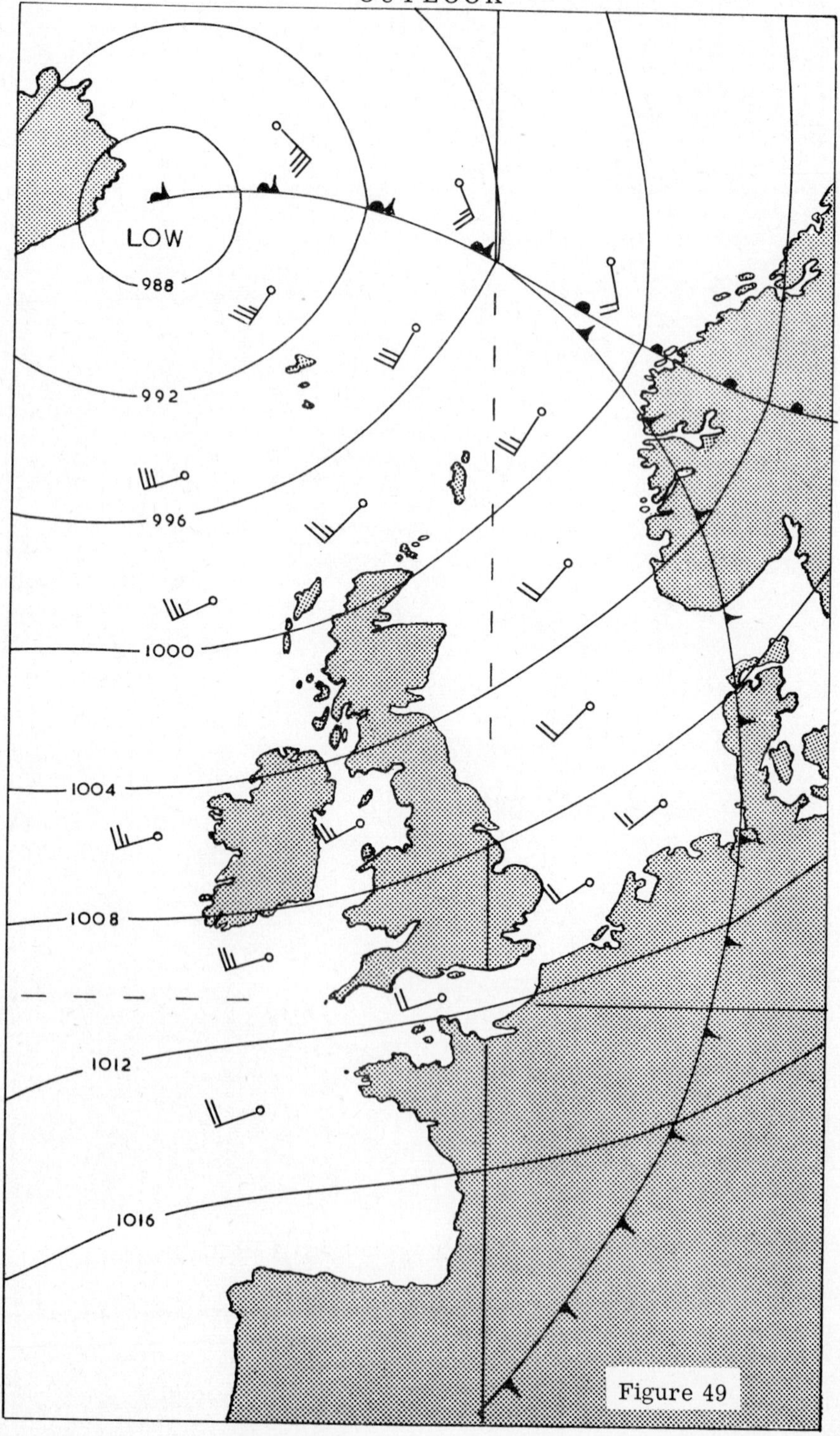

Figure 49

A SECONDARY COLD FRONT

A secondary cold front is occasionally formed in addition to the primary warm and cold fronts which enclose the warm sector of a depression. It forms in the cold air behind the primary cold front and is a character-istic of polar or arctic air.

The cold air in the rear of a cold front tends to lose its polar characteristics after a while. If the prevailing pressure pattern is such that a fresh supply of polar air, following a more direct path from the polar regions, flows in towards the primary cold front a secondary cold front will be formed. This secondary cold front will be marked by changes in the temperature and moisture content of the air and as this occurs along a clearly defined line a trough of low pressure is set up.

The weather associated with a secondary cold front is similar to that at the primary cold front, namely cumuliform clouds and showery weather. On occasions it will show the characteristics of a line squall.

A secondary cold front may also form in the rear of an occluded front, figure 50, when the older polar air between these two fronts then acts as a warm sector and thus regenerates the occluded depression.

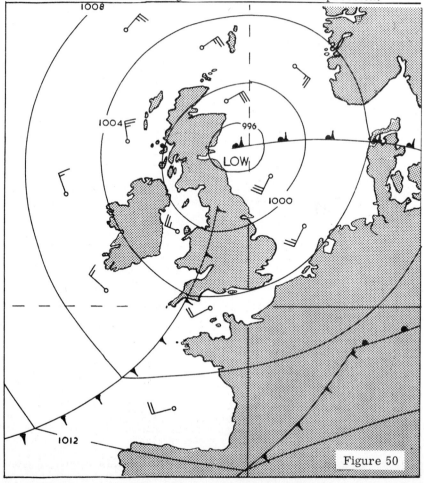

Figure 50

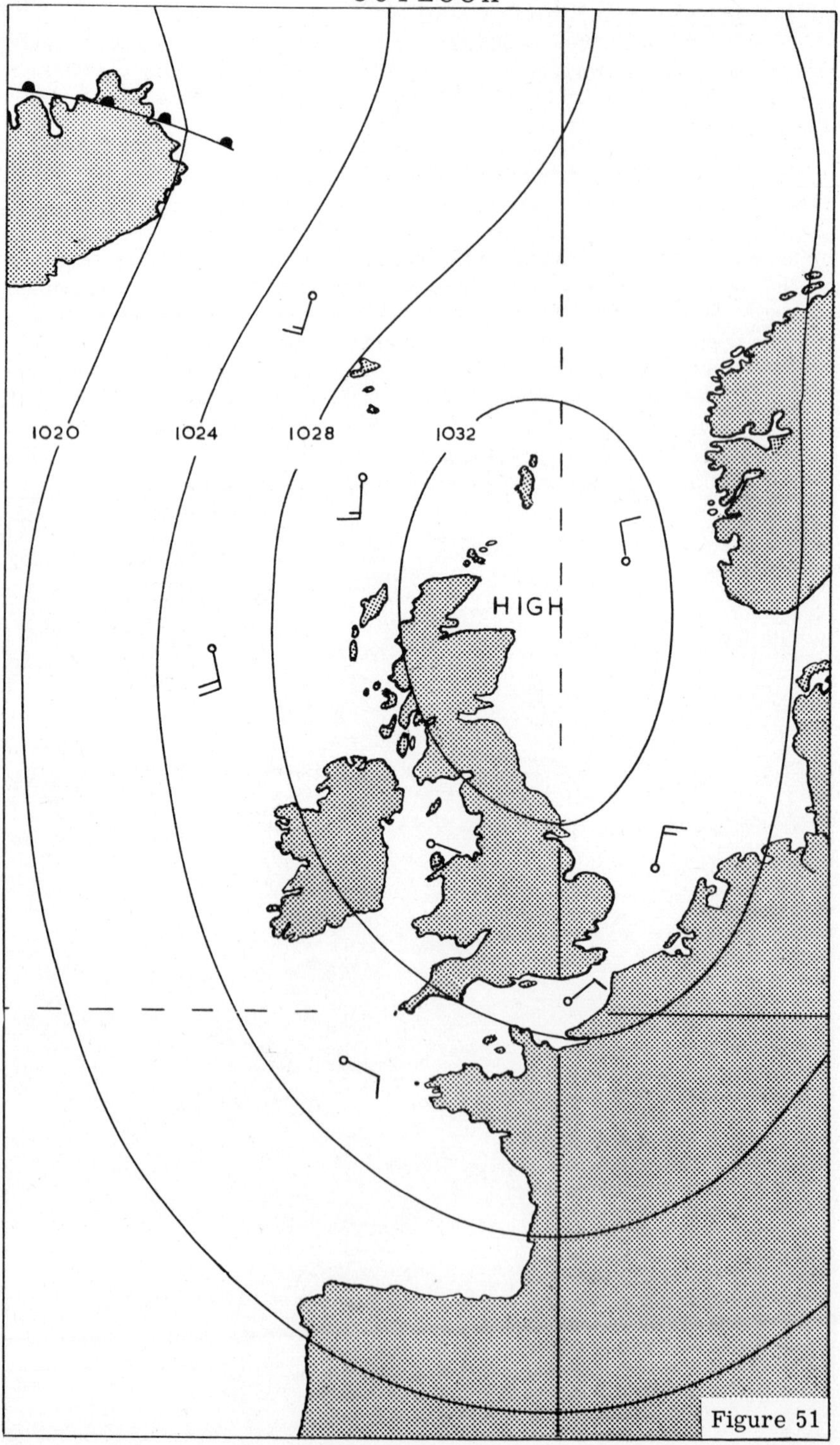

Figure 51

ANTICYCLONES

Anticyclones are areas of high barometric pressure, the wind circulating in a clockwise direction (northern hemisphere) around the centre. They are shown on a weather chart as a system of closed isobars, figure 51, high pressure at the centre decreasing outwards and generally with weak or slack 'pressure gradients giving rise to light winds.

Anticyclones may be subdivided into two types; these are the 'semi-permanent' and the 'migratory' or 'temporary' types. The Azores High referred to on page 17 is of the former type and is shown in many of the figures. Anticyclones which form, persist for a day, possibly longer, and are then replaced by other pressure systems are of the latter type.

Movement of air within a depression

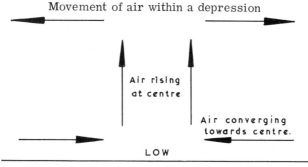

Air rising
at centre

Air converging
towards centre.

LOW

Figure 52

Figure 52 shows the general movement of air within a depression, namely rising at the centre and along the fronts with the air at the surface converging towards the centre. As has already been shown this rising air results in cloud and precipitation.

The movement of the air within an anticyclone is such that the air aloft flows in towards the centre, then slowly sinks or subsides, finally flowing outwards, namely diverging, at the surface, see figure 53.

The air subsiding within an anticyclone warms, its capacity for water vapour increases, and there is a tendency for clouds to thin out and disperse thus giving rise to clear skies.

Anticyclones are generally regions of fine weather, clear skies and light winds.

Movement of air within an anticyclone

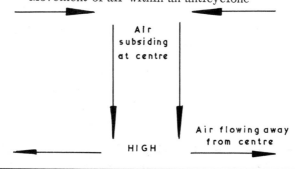

Air
subsiding
at centre

Air flowing away
from centre

HIGH

Figure 53

Figure 51 shows the general pressure distribution associated with anticyclones of the temporary type and figure 54 shows an extension of the Azores High towards the British Isles.

Clear skies may give rise to the formation of fog over the land at night, most noticeable during the autumn and spring when the long clear nights give rise to prolonged cooling of the ground. Once the temperature of the surface falls below the dew point temperature of the surrounding air, condensation will take place with the likelihood of fog forming. Such fog, forming after sunset, may not clear until well after sunrise and may even persist all day with a re-formation or thickening after sunset. Radiation or land fog, as this is called, frequently forms in valleys and then may spread outwards to cover the approaches to these regions.

Typical examples of this are the fogs which form in the Thames valley and then spread outwards to cover the Thames estuary and Dover Strait and those of the Clyde Valley which spread over the Firth of Clyde. Such fogs can seriously hamper the movement of shipping and thus bring ports to a standstill.

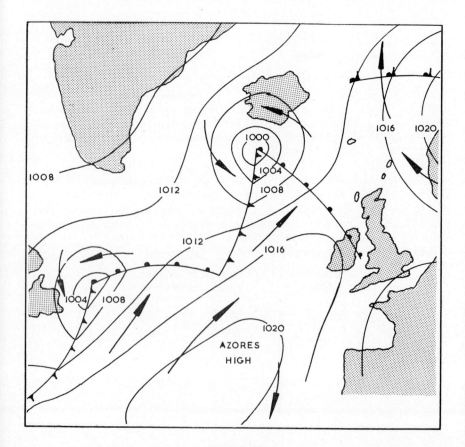

Figure 54

Although clear skies are generally associated with the weather of anticyclones, occasionally moist air may drift inland from over the sea. Turbulence may cause this air to be lifted above the level at which condensation takes place giving rise to cumulus clouds. Frequently these clouds spread out horizontally to form a layer of stratocumulus clouds which tend to disappear or reduce in thickness by night, reforming or thickening after sunrise. During the winter months this type of cloud is slow to clear since the sun is low in the sky and has little strength; then cold, dull, gloomy weather may be experienced.

The cloud is prevented from rising and dispersing by a temperature inversion just above the cloud layer brought about by the warming of the air within the anticyclone as it subsides (figure 55). Should fog have formed initially, with the cloud spreading in overhead, then this cloud coverage may prevent the dispersal of the fog during the daytime.

Turbulence Cloud

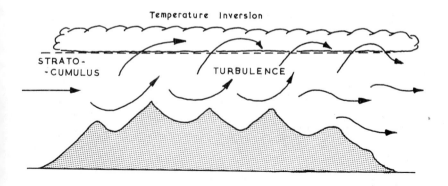

Figure 55

EXAMPLE 10

The General Synopsis
"An anticyclone covers the British Isles and will remain almost stationary during the next 24 hours ".

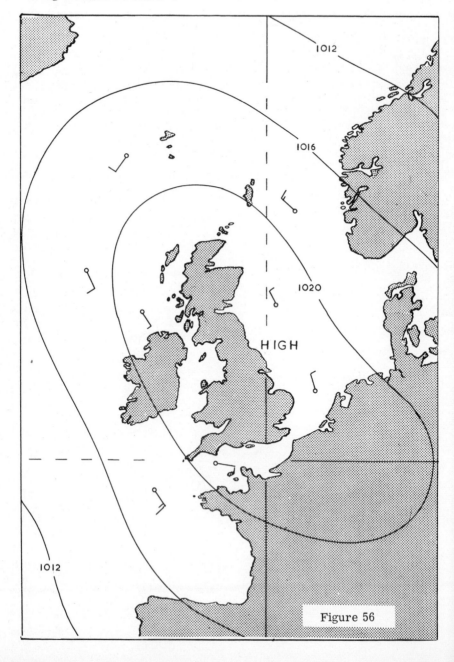

Figure 56

Figure 56 shows the general pressure distribution and prevailing winds for the above synopsis.

A weak or slack pressure gradient over the whole area, except for southwest Ireland will give rise to calms or light variable winds. Over the southern part of Ireland the gradient is slightly steeper as a depression approaches from the Atlantic giving a gentle or moderate breeze in that area.

The weather will generally be dry with clear skies in the southern part of the region but overcast skies with the possibility of light rain or drizzle may be experienced to the north of Scotland.

Bright intervals during the day will possibly be replaced by fog during the night over much of England, Wales and Northern Ireland.

A RIDGE OF HIGH PRESSURE

A ridge of high pressure may extend outwards in any direction from an anticyclone. Figure 57 illustrates a narrow ridge lying between two depressions whereas figure 58 illustrates a broad ridge extending northeast from the Azores to cover the British Isles. Figure 57 also shows another ridge extending southeasterly from a high to the west of Iceland.

The weather associated with a ridge of high pressure may be similar to that of an anticyclone, or may be just a short period of bright weather between the passage of one depression and the arrival of the next. Occasionally the ridge lying between two depressions may be relatively broad giving rise to a spell of anticyclonic weather.

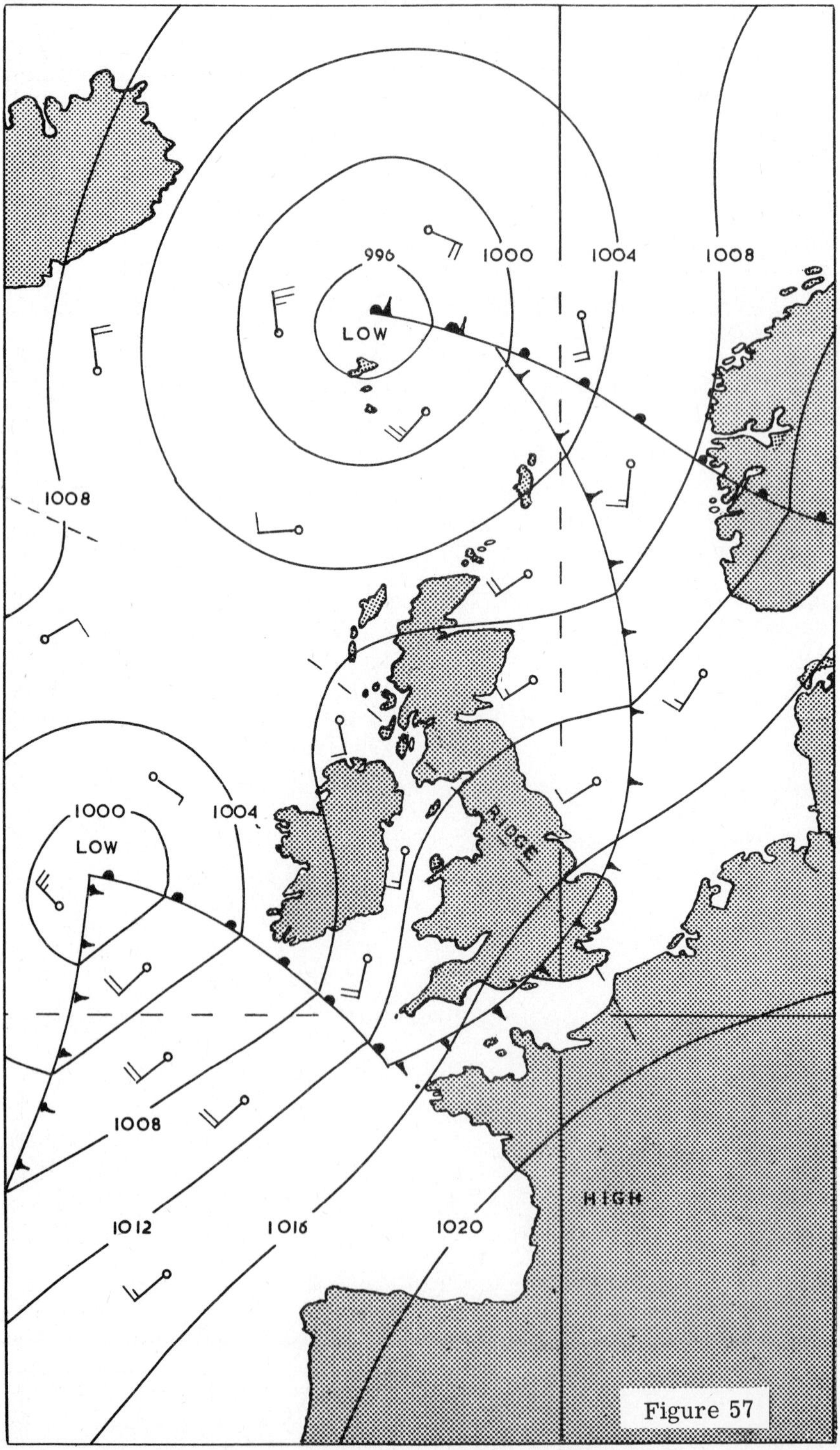

Figure 57

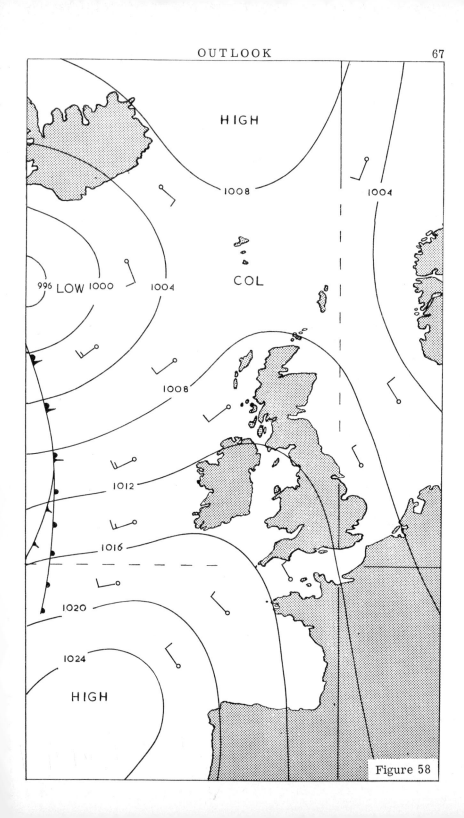

Figure 58

EXAMPLE 11

The General Synopsis

" A depression to the south of Iceland is almost stationary and the associated trough has cleared all parts of the British Isles. A weak depression to the west of Ireland is expected to move northeast and to be centred over the north of Scotland bringing a warm front across all regions during the next 24 hours. A weak ridge of high pressure is affecting all regions ".

Figure 59 shows the general pressure distribution and prevailing winds for the above synopsis.

Winds will be generally light to moderate over all regions with pressure rising slowly before the ridge. NW'ly winds, before the ridge, will back to the SW on the passage of the ridge with a falling barometer.

Eastern districts will be dry and sunny at first but cloud and rain in the west will slowly spread to all regions as the ridge moves eastwards into the North Sea to be replaced by the depression to the west of Ireland.

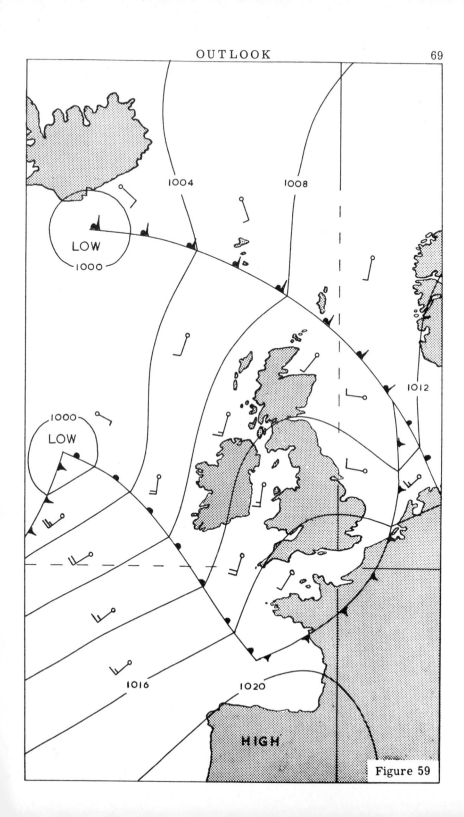

Figure 59

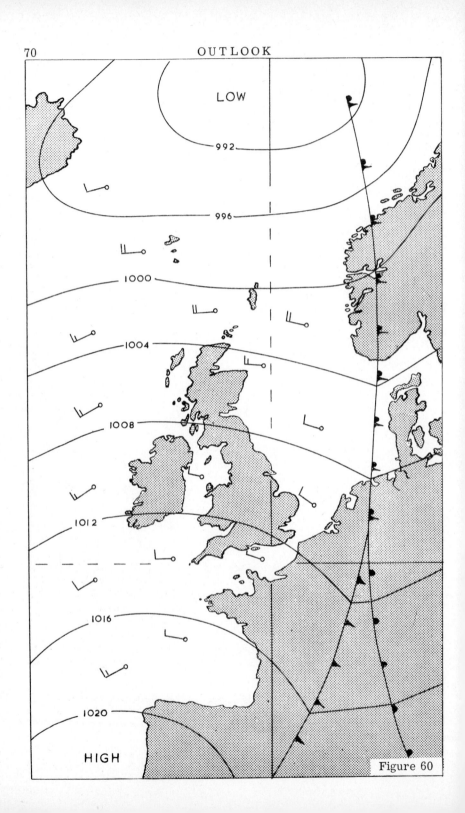

Figure 60

EXAMPLE 12

The General Synopsis

" A ridge of high pressure extends over England and Wales from a large anticyclone centred near the Azores. A depression to the northeast of Iceland has its associated trough lying over Scandinavia and the eastern side of the North Sea ".

Figure 60 shows the general pressure distribution and prevailing winds associated with the above synopsis. Winds are generally moderate to light over the whole region with a predominantly westerly air stream.

The type of weather associated with this synopsis is similar to that described in example 4, page 24.

Generally dull, wet weather will affect all areas of the British Isles although brighter, showery, weather may be expected to the south and east of the region.

A COL

A ' Col ' is an area of small and variable pressure gradients lying between two high and two low pressure areas which are diametrically opposite each other. Figure 61 shows this arrangement of highs and lows with the col lying between them.

Since there are frequently two air streams of different origins flowing into such an area the weather will be unsettled with the possibility of localised disturbances taking place. In figure 61 cold polar air is flowing down from the north around the high off Iceland to meet the warm air flowing up from the south around the high situated over the Iberian Peninsula.

Weak or slack pressure gradients give rise to calm and light variable winds within the col. During the summer months stagnation of the air within this region will give rise to hot sultry weather and outbreaks of thunderstorms during the latter part of the afternoon and early evening. In winter, with the possibility of clear skies and light winds, fog or mist patches may be expected.

When the col forms between two depressions which are moving fairly rapidly over the region the above weather sequence may hardly be noticeable and the pattern of weather experienced is that associated with the passage of depressions, rear cold front weather being succeeded by pre-warm front weather.

A col is of more interest to the forecaster in anticipating the possibility of localised changes in the general weather and also in the forecasting of the movements of a depression since it forms an easy path for a depression to follow.

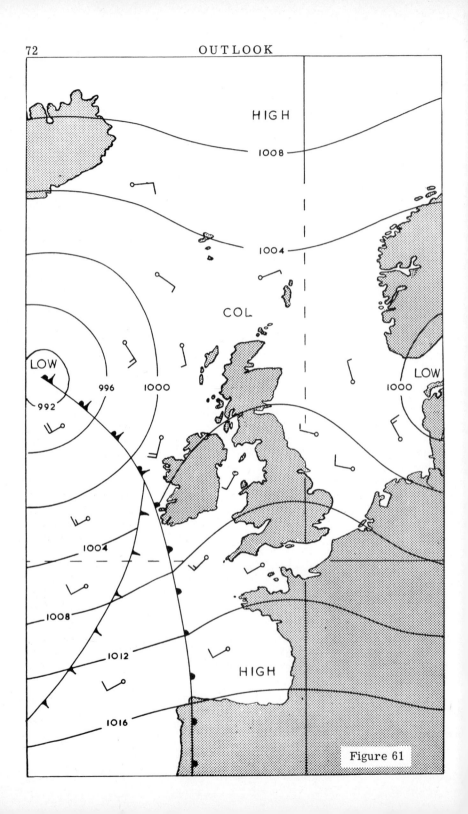

Figure 61

EXAMPLE 13

The General Synopsis

"A low pressure area extending from Norway to eastern France is moving slowly east whilst a weak ridge of high pressure covers the British Isles. A trough of low pressure to the west of the British Isles is moving slowly east".

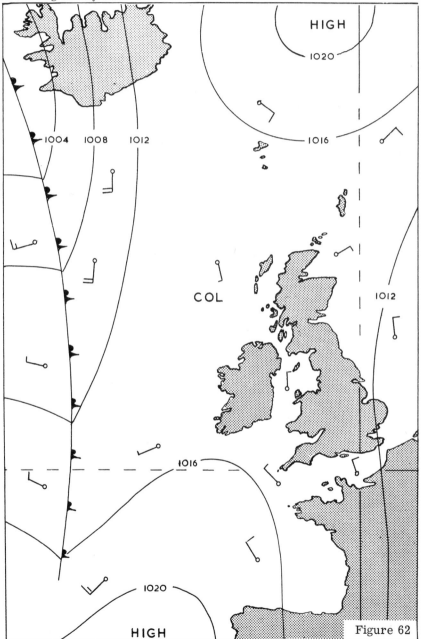

Figure 62

Figure 62 shows the general pressure distribution and prevailing winds associated with the above synopsis. The weak ridge of high pressure covering the British Isles is similar to a col. Indeterminate pressure gradients over the whole region have given rise to calms almost everywhere.

To the west of the region, over Ireland, the west coast of Scotland and England it will generally be cloudy with occasional rain as the trough approaches from the west. The remaining parts of Scotland will be generally cloudy with showery weather since they are influenced by the high to the north of Scotland. East and southeast England will generally be fine and sunny with fog forming after sunset.

The general outlook is cloud and rain at times in the west, dry in the east with fog at night and in the early morning.

4

CLOUD AND PRECIPITATION

The formation of cloud and precipitation (rain, snow etc.) has already been described in previous chapters in association with particular pressure systems and the prevailing air stream. Their formation is now given, under separate headings, with the different ways in which they may occur.

CLOUDS

These are formed by the initial rising of moist air. As this air rises it expands and cools; eventually the air becomes saturated and further cooling, as the air continues to rise, results in the condensation of the excess water vapour into minute water droplets. These are visible as cloud.

The initial rising of the air may be brought about in the following ways:-

1. convection currents due to surface heating;
2. turbulent motion over undulating ground;
3. orographic ascent;
4. frontal activity between different air masses.

1. CONVECTION CLOUDS

Convection currents, within a relatively cold air mass, may be caused by the localised heating of the air at the surface. These rising currents of air produce the well known cumuliform clouds, i.e. cumulus and cumulonimbus. The depths of these clouds may vary between a few thousand feet (fair weather cumulus) and many thousands of feet (the towering cumulonimbus). Strong convection currents are experienced within these towering clouds attaining speeds of up to 150 feet per second, see figure 63.

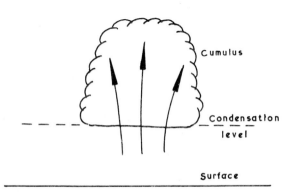

Figure 63

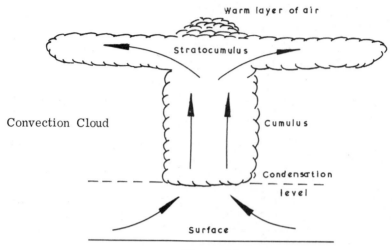

Figure 64

Should these rising currents of air meet a layer in which the air, at that level, is warmer than the temperature of the rising air, the vertical motion is halted and the cloud tops spread out horizontally to form a layer of stratocumulus, altocumulus, or anvil cirrus, see figures 64 and 65.

Convection clouds are typical of the type of cloud which forms on a summer's afternoon and especially those associated with thunderstorms, see page 88.

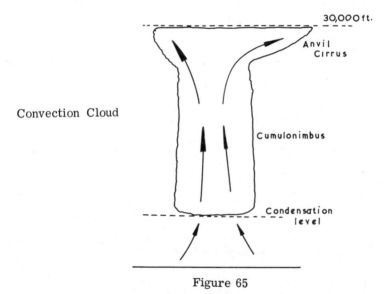

Figure 65

2.   TURBULENT CLOUDS

Moist air, which has drifted inland, may be carried upwards by turbulence. The rising air cools and should it be carried above the condensation level it will become saturated and condensation will take place with the formation of cloud. A necessary condition with turbulent cloud is that the temperature of the air above the condensation level is higher than that of the rising air. This warm layer of air prevents the air from rising of its own free will and it therefore spreads out horizontally forming a layer of stratiform cloud, i.e. stratus and stratocumulus cloud, see figure 66.

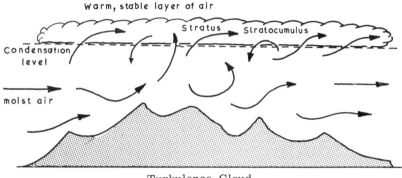

Turbulence Cloud
Figure 66

3.   OROGRAPHIC CLOUDS

When moist air is forced to rise on meeting a range of mountains, hills or high coastlines, it cools, becomes saturated and further cooling as the air continues to rise results in condensation and the formation of stratiform cloud. The tops of the hills may then be shrouded in cloud, figure 67, or if the condensation level is above the summit, the cloud

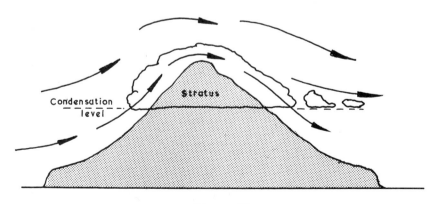

Figure 67

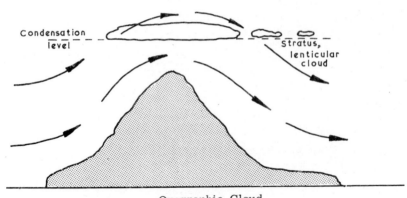

Orographic Cloud

Figure 68

may form above this point, figures 68 and 69, as the air over the summit is raised above its condensation level.

Orographic ascent may trigger off convection currents; should the rising air be warmer than the surrounding free air cumuliform clouds may well result.

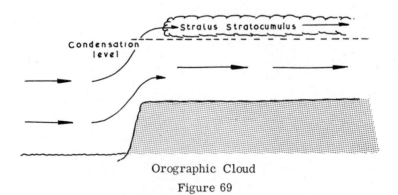

Orographic Cloud

Figure 69

4.   FRONTAL CLOUDS

As shown on page 38 the type of cloud associated with a front depends on whether the front is of the warm or cold type.

(a)   WARM FRONT CLOUDS

The warm air rising over the colder air cools as it ascends finally becoming saturated. Further cooling as the air continues to rise results in condensation and the formation of cloud. Cloud formed in this way may extend for many miles ahead of the front and rise to a height of many thousands of feet. The cloud sequence, as shown in figure 70, is cirrus, cirrostratus, altostratus and nimbostratus.

Figure 70

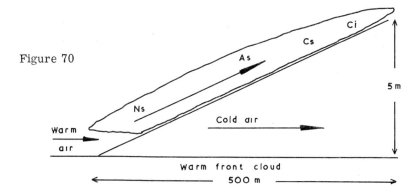

Warm front cloud

(b)   COLD FRONT CLOUDS

The cold advancing air mass undercuts the warmer air before the front, lifts it off the ground and thus sets up strong convection currents since the warmer air on rising meets colder air. These strong convection currents soon bring about saturation, condensation and the formation of cumuliform clouds, i. e. cumulus and cumulonimbus clouds, see figure 71.

Figure 71

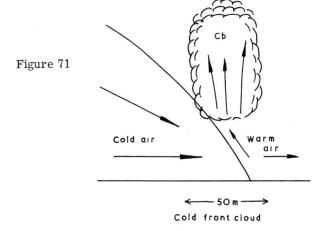

Cold front cloud

THE CLASSIFICATION OF CLOUDS

The main types of cloud and the heights at which they occur are listed below. A description of these cloud types has already been given and against each cloud type is the page number on which it may be found.

HIGH CLOUDS

18, 000 feet and above

Cirrus	Ci.	page 38
Cirrostratus	Cs.	page 38
Cirrocumulus	Cc.	page 43

OUTLOOK
MEDIUM CLOUDS

between 8,000 feet and 18,000 feet

Altocumulus   Ac. page 39
Altostratus   As. page 39

LOW CLOUDS

below 8,000 feet.

Stratocumulus Sc. page 25
Nimbostratus Ns. page 39
Stratus   St. page 21

CLOUDS EXTENDING FROM JUST ABOVE THE SURFACE TO GREAT HEIGHTS

Cumulus   Cu. page 19
CumulonimbusCb. page 19

THE DAILY VARIATION IN THE CLOUD AMOUNT

Cumulus clouds which have formed during the daytime in summer, due to solar heating, may soon disappear after sunset. As the surface cools the convection currents soon cease and with no further rising air to maintain the cloud formation they soon dissipate giving way to clear skies. This condition is most noticeable during anticyclonic conditions and especially over the land rather than over the sea since here there is only a small change of temperature at the surface between night and day.

On the other hand stratocumulus cloud which has formed by turbulence may disappear or reduce in thickness by day, reforming or thickening again after sunset. During the daytime the air is warmed, the condensation level is then raised and should this rise above the level to which turbulence extends the clouds will disappear. At night as the temperature decreases the cloud may reform, this reformation being assisted both by cooling from below and the radiation of heat to space from the cloud layer.

PRECIPITATION

It does not necessarily mean that the formation of cloud will be followed by precipitation, quite the contrary in fact. Large clouds may develop and yet no precipitation takes place. Two theories have become established regarding the formation of precipitation although much more research has yet to be carried out on this subject. The two theories are the Bergeron Theory and the Coalescence Theory. The former states that all rain commences as snow and the latter covers those cases where rain is known to fall from a cloud whose temperature, even at the top, does not fall below freezing point. A brief description of these two theories follows.

BERGERON THEORY

When moist air rises it cools and may finally become saturated. Further cooling results in condensation taking place with the formation of cloud.

Initially the water droplets may be at a temperature above freezing but as the height increases the temperature decreases until it falls below freezing point. Above this level, the freezing level, the water droplets may be in a supercooled state but since there is a strong tendency for supercooled droplets to turn to ice crystals there will be a region within the cloud where there are both supercooled droplets and ice crystals existing together. These may exist for a height of many thousands of feet. The ice crystals will absorb the supercooled droplets forming bigger ice crystals and at the top of the cloud only ice crystals will exist. These ice crystals join together to form snowflakes and when large enough they begin to descend through the cloud. Further growth takes place as the supercooled droplets freeze on to the snowflakes increasing their size. Below the freezing level the snowflakes thaw to form water droplets which descend as rain. Figure 72 shows the above process in diagrammatic form.

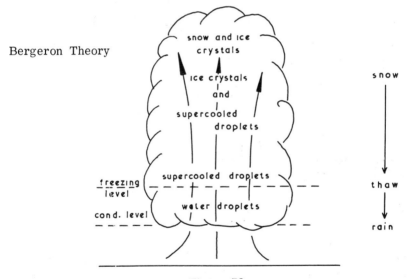

Figure 72

COALESCENCE THEORY

A necessary condition for the rain making process to take effect is that the clouds have a high moisture content and also that the water droplets of which the cloud is composed vary in size. The larger droplets attract the smaller droplets and thus grow in size. Since there is a limit to the size of a water droplet, 5 to 7 mm. in diameter, these larger droplets break up into smaller droplets which in turn grow in size, break up, grow in size etc., a chain reaction being set up. Finally the drops overcome the frictional resistance of the air and fall to the ground as rain.

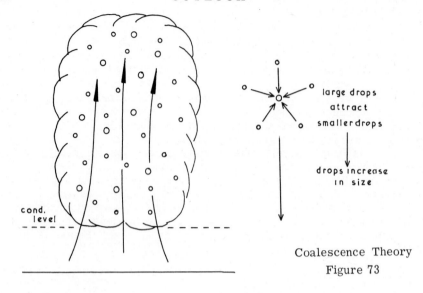

Coalescence Theory
Figure 73

The updrafts within the cloud must be relatively slow so that there is ample time for droplet growth to take place, see figure 73.

An idea of the size of a cloud droplet may be gathered from the fact that there over a million cloud droplets to each normal sized raindrop of 1 to 2 mm. in diameter.

The type of rainfall experienced may be associated with the way in which the clouds have been formed as given below.

CONVECTIONAL RAIN

Very moist air giving rise to cumuliform clouds results in heavy rain even thunderstorms. Showers associated with polar air streams are of this nature and usually occur during the late afternoon and evening over the land but may occur at any time of the day or night over the sea.

TURBULENCE RAIN

Turbulence cloud may give rise to light rain or drizzle but it is not a frequent occurrence.

OROGRAPHIC RAIN

Stratus cloud forming on the windward side of high ground gives rise to some of the largest amounts of rainfall known. The western side of the British Isles has a far greater rainfall than that of the east coast since the prevailing winds over the British Isles are from a westerly direction. The rainfall is often of a continuous nature lasting for a long period of time.

FRONTAL RAIN

This rainfall occurs within a depression and may occur at any time of the day or night depending on the passage of the respective front.

The rainfall associated with a warm front is of a continuous nature before the passage of the front; it ceases at the front although there may be slight rain or drizzle in its rear. At a cold front with strong convection currents resulting from the interaction of the differing air masses heavy rain may occur with perhaps even thunder and hail. The heavy rain is for only a relatively short period of time although showery weather is usually experienced in the rear of the cold front.

In addition to precipitation in the form of rain and snow there might also be hail or sleet, as well as precipitation on to a surface in the form of dew and frost. These various forms of precipitation are as follows:-

Snow: Should condensation take place at temperatures below freezing point ice crystals are formed. The first ice crystals formed are very small and as they join together snowflakes are formed. An examination of a snowflake shows it to be composed of very many small ice crystals. The crystals do not melt on their way from the cloud to the surface.

Hail: Within a cloud, especially of the cumulonimbus type, ice crystals and supercooled water droplets exist together. Collision between the ice crystals and supercooled droplets due to the strong air currents prevailing throughout the cloud causes the supercooled droplets to freeze around the ice crystals forming small ice pellets. If these ice pellets are carried upwards into the snow region of the cloud the snowflakes attach themselves to the ice pellets forming hailstones.

Since strong vertical currents are required within the cloud for the hailstones to grow in size they are usually associated with convectional type clouds, i.e. cumulonimbus.

Dew: If moist air is cooled it will eventually become saturated and further cooling will result in the excess water vapour condensing into water droplets. When this cooling is by contact with a cold surface the resulting condensation is called dew.

Hoar Frost: If the condensation of water vapour does not begin until the temperature of the air is below freezing point the initial waterdrops soon freeze and further condensation is then directly to ice forming a layer of soft white ice crystals when deposited on the surface.

Glazed Frost: When rain falls on to a surface which has a temperature below freezing point the rain drops freeze forming a sheet of clear ice. The rain drops are frequently in the supercooled state and the freezing of these water droplets is slow enough for a film of water to form initially.

Rime: This occurs when supercooled water drops freeze on coming into contact with a surface which has a temperature below freezing point. It occurs in freezing fog (wet fog) when the fog particles are composed of supercooled droplets. The deposit of ice which forms grows out to windward of exposed objects.

Sleet: This is the term given to rain and snow falling together or snow being partially melted on arrival at the surface.

VISIBILITY

When moist air is cooled sufficiently it becomes saturated and further cooling results in the excess water vapour condensing to form water droplets. Condensation taking place just above the surface results in the formation of mist or fog. The difference between the two depends on the degree of visibility; if visibility is below 1,100 yards it is said to be foggy, between 1,100 yards and 2,200 yards misty, and above 2,200 yards poor, moderate, good, very good or excellent as the case may be.

Fog may be one of a number of types, these are (1) Advection or Sea Fog, (2) Radiation or Land Fog, (3) Sea Smoke or Warm Water Fog and (4) Frontal Fog.

ADVECTION OR SEA FOG

When warm moist air flows over a relatively cold sea surface the temperature of the air in contact with this surface is lowered. Should the sea temperature be below the dew point temperature of the air, cooling will continue until the air is saturated. Further cooling results in condensation taking place with the formation of mist or fog. Fogs formed in this way are frequently experienced around the coasts of the British Isles and may persist even with strong winds, see figure 74.

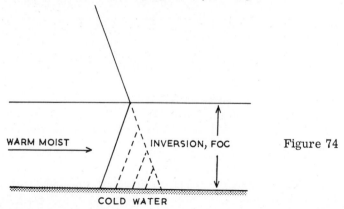

Figure 74

Fog of this nature may also occur when warm moist air flows over a land which has been previously cooled or is covered with snow. Fog formed over the land in this way is unlikely to persist and is usually confined to the time of the onset of the warm wind. It may occur in the British Isles during the winter when easterly winds are replaced by warm south-westerly winds.

RADIATION OR LAND FOG

A clear sky at night results in the land being cooled by radiation to space and likewise the air in contact with the surface is also cooled. Should the surface temperature fall below the dew point temperature of the air saturation will occur, and as the temperature falls still further condensation will take place with the formation of fog. Cooling by radiation from the fog as well as from the surface helps to increase the depth of the fog. Such fog forming in valleys may drift out to sea, i.e. Thames Estuary and Approaches, Firth of Clyde, etc.

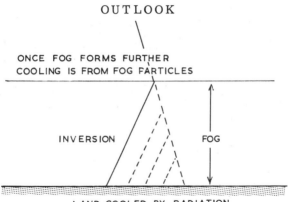

ONCE FOG FORMS FURTHER
COOLING IS FROM FOG PARTICLES

INVERSION   FOG

LAND COOLED BY RADIATION
Figure 75

The ideal conditions for the formation of this type of fog are:-

(a) a clear night sky to permit of the maximum amount of cooling, preferably the long winter nights;

(b) the presence of moist air at sunset, a frequent occurrence in autumn and winter especially after a showery afternoon or at places near to open water;

(c) a light wind to give just sufficient turbulence to the air so that the water droplets are held in suspension.

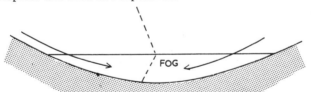

FOG

FOG TENDING TO SETTLE IN VALLEYS
Figure 76

Anticyclonic conditions are most favourable to the formation of this type of fog. Valleys sheltered from the prevailing wind permit pools of cold air to collect and fog may then form under such conditions.

SEA SMOKE OR WARM WATER FOG

This is a similar occurrence to that of steam rising from the surface of hot water and occurs when there is a large temperature difference between the air and the water, usually in the region of 10° C or 18° F.

Cold air flowing over warm water absorbs moisture by direct evaporation from the surface of the water. The low temperature of the air

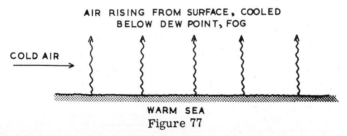

AIR RISING FROM SURFACE, COOLED
BELOW DEW POINT, FOG

COLD AIR

WARM SEA
Figure 77

means that only a small amount of water vapour need be absorbed for the air to become saturated. The lowest layers of this cold air are also heated by conduction from contact with the warmer water and since colder air lies above the surface this warm air rises by convection. As the air rises it immediately comes in contact with the colder air, is rapidly cooled to below its dew point temperature and condensation takes place with the formation of fog as shown in figure 77.

The fog appears as steam rising from the surface of the water and although its height is generally below 30 feet it may attain much greater heights.

FRONTAL FOG

The passage of a warm front is occasionally accompanied by widespread fog. This may occur if the temperature of the air before the front is very low, the fog being due to the mixing of the warm and cold air at the front. It usually takes the form of very low cloud which envelops high ground and may fall to sea level as fog.

Fog may also form by the mixing of two different air currents. An easterly current off the Continent mixing with a southwesterly current from the Atlantic may give rise to a belt of fog. In winter and spring the southwesterly current is warm and moist whereas the easterly current is very cold and dry. Such fogs are liable to occur whenever air streams of widely different origin flow side by side, as may be experienced within a col.

THUNDERSTORMS

These are liable to occur when strong convection currents are set up within an air mass. These strong upcurrents, existing to a height of at least 10,000 feet, give rise to the formation of cumulonimbus cloud and may be caused by:-

(a)   the heating of the ground by solar radiation, or

(b)   cold air at the surface undercutting warmer air.

Thunderstorms which occur in the late afternoon and evening during the summer months are usually caused by the heating of the ground during the day by solar radiation. They are frequently associated with a polar maritime air stream since cold air then overlies the warmer surface air, an ideal condition for the formation of strong convection currents and the necessary cloud development, figure 78.

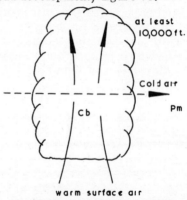

Localised Heating

Figure 78

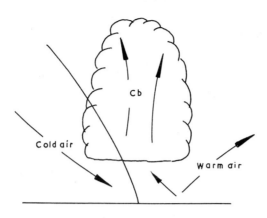

Frontal Activity

Figure 79

When cold air undercuts warmer air as at a cold front the warmer air is lifted off the surface. As it rises it meets with the colder air aloft and strong convection currents are set up which may give rise to thunderstorms. Thunderstorms of this nature may occur at any time depending on the passage of the cold front, figure 79.

Thunderstorms may also occur over the sea when relatively cold air is heated in its passage over a warmer sea. Such storms may then occur at any time of the day or night.

The life cycle of a thunderstorm is relatively short lasting approximately 20 to 30 minutes but, since groups of storms usually form, thunderstorms may persist for a number of hours. The life cycle of a thunderstorm may be described in three stages as follows:

1.   The 'growing' stage.
The strong rising currents give rise to the formation of cumulonimbus cloud, rain drops forming within the cloud.

2.   The 'mature' stage.
The rain drops, plus the possibility of hailstones, grow in size and finally become too heavy to be supported by the ascending air currents and start to descend. This great weight of water plus the hailstones drags cold air down with it. The rain and, or, hailstones plus the down draught of cold air reach the ground together, the cold air spreading out laterally which is felt as a cold gusty wind.

3.   The 'decaying' stage.
This downdraught of cold air gradually spreads throughout the cloud, the precipitation decreases and the cloud dissipates. The energy of the thunderstorm, namely the rising moist air, is cut off as the area of downdraught spreads throughout the cloud. This is shown in figure 80.

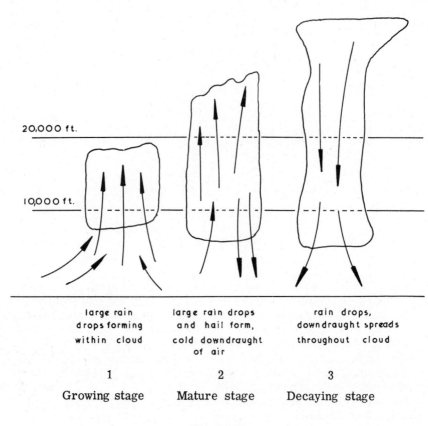

20,000 ft.

10,000 ft.

large rain drops forming within cloud	large rain drops and hail form, cold downdraught of air	rain drops, downdraught spreads throughout cloud
1	2	3
Growing stage	Mature stage	Decaying stage

Figure 80

LIGHTNING AND THUNDER

Lightning is a discharge of static electricity and may take place between a cloud and the ground or between two clouds. The flash of lightning is simply an enormous spark and the thunder is the sound produced by the rapid expansion of the air as it is suddenly and intensely heated along the path of the lightning flash.

5

LOCAL WINDS

LAND AND SEA BREEZES

Along the coast changes in the wind direction and speed are a characteristic feature, especially on fine sunny days and clear nights. During the daytime an onshore or sea breeze may be experienced to be replaced at night by an offshore or land breeze.

These local winds are brought about by the unequal heating and cooling of the land and sea. By day the land is heated to a greater extent than the sea, reference page 12, so that the air over the land rises in temperature, becomes less dense and expands. This expansion causes a slight increase in pressure aloft which in turn gives rise to a slight drift of the air from the land towards the sea at this level. This drift reduces the pressure slightly over the land and increases it to seaward. A pressure gradient is thus set up at the surface, low pressure over the land relative to the sea and an onshore wind results.

At night the wind directions are reversed, cooling of the land due to radiation results in a general contraction of the air in the lowest layers as it cools and an increase in the surface density. Pressure builds up over the land relative to the sea and results in an offshore or land breeze.

The reversal of these winds takes place between 500 feet and 1,000 feet above the surface although the winds at this level are not very well defined.

Around the British Isles the strength of these winds is relatively light, the onshore wind attaining speeds up to 10 knots and the offshore wind speeds up to 5 knots. Occasionally the offshore wind may be accelerated by a katabatic effect. They extend up to distances of 10 to 15 miles either side of the coastline, the onshore breeze commencing in the late morning and lasting until just after sunset and the offshore breeze commencing during the late evening lasting until sunrise. Since a light prevailing wind and fine weather are necessary for their occurrence they are a feature of anticyclonic weather.

KATABATIC WINDS

These generally occur at night since a necessary condition for their formation is that the ground and the air in contact with it is colder than that at the same level in the free atmosphere.

At night when the sky is clear the ground cools by radiation and likewise the air in contact with the ground cools. When this air becomes colder and therefore denser than the air at the same level in the free atmosphere it starts to sink and gives rise to a wind which blows downhill.

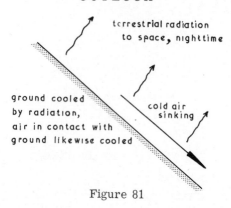

Figure 81

Even on a gently sloping ground a katabatic effect may be felt on clear nights draining cold air into low lying regions. On mountain slopes this katabatic effect is greatly increased and should the ground be covered by snow or ice it may also occur during the daytime.

Quite strong winds are produced by this effect and may even attain gale force when conditions are ideal, especially when there is a drainage effect of this cold air into a valley which opens out to the sea, see figure 81.

FÖHN WIND

This is a relatively warm dry wind which may be felt to leeward of high ground. Although the name refers to a local wind experienced in the Alps it has also become the general name for such a wind.

Moist air forced to rise on meeting the side of a mountain barrier cools and if this barrier is of sufficient height the air is cooled below its dew point temperature and condensation with the formation of cloud and rain takes place. On reaching the summit the air descends on the lee side and warms in descent. Since precipitation took place to windward and thus a large amount of water vapour has been removed from the air, the air temperature soon rises above its dew point temperature and the descending air continues to warm, finally reaching the ground as a relatively warm dry wind, see figure 82.

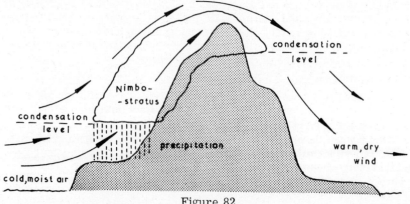

Figure 82

Unsaturated air cools in ascent, warms in descent, at a higher rate (5·4° F per 1,000 ft. or 3° C per 1,000 ft.) than saturated air (between 3° F and 5·4° F per 1,000 ft. or 2° C and 3° C per 1,000 ft.). The reason for this temperature difference is that as saturated air cools there is a release of heat as condensation takes place. The heat loss due to the air rising and expanding is thus partly offset by this gain of heat due to condensation.

A föhn wind is frequently experienced in Scotland when, with a south-westerly air stream, condensation, cloud and precipitation takes place on the western side of the highlands and a warm dry wind is felt on the eastern side. Other occasions when this may occur will be evident to the reader.

Under ideal conditions, increases of temperature of up to 10°C (18° F) may be experienced between the two sides of a mountain barrier.

6

FORECASTING

Accurate forecasting of the weather requires many years of experience and a detailed knowledge of both surface and upper air conditions at a large number of reporting stations within the area covered by the forecast. Once this information has been collected together and a forecast made its reliability will depend on the time interval for which it is required. A forecast covering the next few hours should be fairly reliable but as the time interval for which the forecast is required increases its reliability decreases.

Forecasts generally cover a fairly wide area and are therefore unable to take local conditions into account. The shipping forecast covers the whole of the British Isles and adjacent waters though forecasts are given for each shipping area but these are only brief giving winds, weather and visibility.

The preceding pages have shown various types of pressure systems, their associated weather and movement across the British Isles. It is essential, when making a forecast, to recognise the prevailing pressure system along with its fronts, if any, and to know the type of weather that may be experienced. Changes that take place within an air mass as it moves from its source region to the observer's locality must be realised since it is these changes which give rise to many important weather phenomena such as cloud, rain, thunderstorms and fog.

The 'amateur' forecaster is concerned not only with the weather as given in the general forecast but more particularly with the weather likely to be experienced in his own locality. The following notes deal initially with the major points to be considered when making a forecast and secondly with any local conditions which may have an appreciable effect on this forecast.

PRESSURE SYSTEMS

The future movements of the pressure systems are usually given in the forecast; this knowledge is essential for a successful forecast.

Depressions generally move in an easterly direction, frequently between north and east, at an average speed of 15 to 20 knots. When the direction of the isobars in the warm sector is known then they may be expected to move parallel to this direction. The centres of low pressure have a tendency to remain over the sea rather than follow a track across the land; they will move up the English Channel or in a southeasterly direction into the North Sea from the vicinity of Iceland. Coastlines and mountain ranges have a strong influence on their movement, slowing them down or causing them to deviate so as to remain over the sea.

Occluded depressions are generally slow moving and may even become stationary. Small depressions, forming within an air mass or on the boundary of a larger depression, are generally fast moving, being carried along in the prevailing air stream. Successive depressions of the same 'family' tend to follow a more southerly track than that taken by the preceding depression whereas occluded depressions tend towards a more northerly track.

Anticyclones, in comparison, are slow moving and tend to drift rather than have a definite movement and are quite liable to remain stationary for many days.

SURFACE WINDS
The strength and direction of the wind depends primarily on the pressure distribution. The direction is anticlockwise around an area of low pressure and clockwise around an area of high pressure in the northern hemisphere. The strength of the wind will depend on the prevailing pressure gradient and for the same gradient the wind strength over the sea is approximately twice as great as that over the land. The angle at which the wind blows to the isobars, the angle of indraft, may be between 10 and 20 degrees over the sea but as high as 30 degrees over the land.

Local effects may have a strong influence on the wind strength and direction and cause the wind to blow in a direction other than that indicated by the isobars. Along the coast stronger winds should be anticipated if off the sea than off the land for the same pressure gradient. Inshore there may be diurnal variations in the strength and direction, the wind tending to veer and strengthen by day, back and lull at night. High ground to windward may have a considerable sheltering effect giving rise to light winds to leeward. Hills may have a deviating effect on the wind direction and valleys a funnelling effect. During the summer, especially under anticyclonic conditions, the land and sea breeze effect may give rise to winds entirely different to those to be expected from the synoptic chart. At night, if conditions are suitable, high ground may give rise to a katabatic effect.

EFFECTS ON WIND DIRECTION AND STRENGTH NEAR THE COAST
(a) A steep coastline tends to deflect onshore winds along the coast with an increase in their strength.
(b) A strong wind blowing directly towards a steep coast may give rise to contrary, gusty winds near to the coast.
(c) A wind approaching a strait or estuary, whose direction is similar to that of the wind, tends to blow along the strait. The wind strength increases as the strait narrows.
(d) An offshore wind is often squally on the leeside of hilly slopes when enhanced at night by the katabatic effect of these slopes. See page 89.
(e) Close to headlands or islands with steep cliffs large changes in the wind direction and strength may be experienced.
(f) The wind direction and strength as shown on a weather map may be affected by localised winds, i.e. land and sea breezes. See page 89.

SEA
Although no mention has been made regarding the state of the sea this is closely related to the wind strength. Since the yachtsman is directly concerned with the prevailing sea conditions this should be included in any forecast for harbours and coastal waters, see page 94.

BEAUFORT SCALE OF WIND FORCE

Beaufort Wind Force	Mean Wind Speed Knots	Descriptive Term	Sea Criterion	Probable Height of Waves in Feet
0	0	Calm	Sea like a mirror	–
1	02	Light air	Ripples with the appearance of scales are formed but without foam crests.	$\frac{1}{4}$
2	05	Light breeze	Small wavelets, still short but more pronounced, crests have a glassy appearance and do not break.	$\frac{1}{2}$
3	09	Gentle breeze	Large wavelets. Crests begin to break. Foam of glassy appearance. Perhaps scattered white horses.	2
4	13	Moderate breeze	Small waves, becoming longer; fairly frequent white horses.	$3\frac{1}{2}$
5	18	Fresh breeze	Moderate waves, taking a more pronounced long form; many white horses are formed. (Chance of some spray)	6
6	24	Strong breeze	Large waves begin to form; the white foam crests are more extensive everywhere. (Probably some spray)	$13\frac{1}{2}$
7	30	Near gale	Sea heaps up and white foam from breaking waves begins to be blown in streaks along the direction of the wind.	18
8	37	Gale	Moderately high waves of greater length; edges of crests begin to break into spindrift. The foam is blown in well-marked streaks along the direction of the wind.	23

Beaufort Wind Force	Mean Wind Speed Knots	Descriptive Term	Sea Criterion	Probable Height of Waves in Feet
9	44	Strong gale	High waves. Dense streaks of foam along the direction of the wind. Crests of waves begin to topple, tumble and roll over. Spray may affect visibility	23
10	52	Storm	Very high waves with long overhanging crests. The resulting foam in great patches is blown in dense white streaks along the direction of the wind. On the whole the surface of the sea takes a white appearance. Tumbling of the sea becomes heavy and shock-like. Visibility affected.	29
11	60	Violent storm	Exceptionally high waves. (Small and medium-sized ships might be lost to view for a time behind the waves.) The sea is completely covered with long white patches of foam lying along the direction of the wind. Everywhere the edges of the wave crests are blown into froth. Visibility affected.	37
12	68	Hurricane	The air is filled with foam and spray. Sea completely white with driving spray; visibility very seriously affected.	45

The column showing the probable height of the waves in feet has been added to show what may be expected in the open sea remote from land. In enclosed waters, or when near land with an off-shore wind, wave heights will be smaller, and the waves steeper.

It must be realised that it may be difficult to estimate the wind force by the sea criterion, especially at night.

The lag effect between the wind getting up and the sea increasing should be borne in mind.

Fetch, depth, swell, heavy rain and tide effects should be considered when estimating the wind force from the appearance of the sea.

CLOUD

The type and amount of cloud will be governed by the prevailing pressure system, the locality strongly influencing the formation of certain types. Frontal activity will give rise to various types and amounts depending on whether the front affecting the area is of the warm, cold or occluded type. Anticyclones, generally associated with clear skies, may have turbulent cloud at night and fair weather cumulus by day. Special attention should be given to the prevailing air stream as this may give rise to the formation of convection and, or, orographic cloud. A prevailing polar air stream will possibly give rise to cumuliform clouds during the day reaching a maximum during the late afternoon and early evening. Orographic clouds form on the windward side of high ground and again special attention should be given to the past history of the prevailing air mass. In the southeast of England large cloud amounts may be experienced with a northeasterly wind off the North Sea, similarly a southwesterly air stream off the West Coast of Scotland will give large amounts of cloud over the western highlands and islands.

PRECIPITATION

The accurate forecasting of precipitation is extremely difficult; it may occur in some areas and not in others although the prevailing conditions may point to general precipitation over the whole area.

Convectional rain may be forecast when a polar air stream covers the region and then takes the form of showers. It occurs mainly over the land during the summer when the sea temperature is comparatively low relative to that inland and it then has its greatest frequency during the late afternoon and early evening. In the winter and spring when the sea temperature is relatively high to that inland, showery weather may be expected over the sea, such showers occurring at any time of the day or night.

Orographic rain may be expected when warm moist air meets a range of hills or a high coastline, the heaviest rainfall occurring on the windward side of the high ground. Even when a moist southwesterly air stream covers the whole of the British Isles, it is probable that the eastern side of the region will be relatively dry. This effect is more noticeable when very high ground lies to windward, i.e. the west and east coasts of Scotland.

Precipitation associated with frontal activity may occur at any time of the day or night with light rain or drizzle in the warm sector. Warm front precipitation is of the continuous type whereas cold front precipitation takes the form of showers.

The passage of air over a cold sea surface may give rise to strato-cumulus cloud and drizzle, a noticeable feature of the east coast of England during the spring with easterly winds off the North Sea.

Precipitation due to one cause may be intensified by another cause; general rainfall may be intensified by orographic effect; orographic uplift may give rise to convectional cloud and rain thus intensifying that due solely to the orographic effect.

Should the surface temperature fall below 37° F snow or sleet may be forecast instead of rain.

VISIBILITY

1.   Sea fog or advection fog

The forecasting of this type of fog is by no means easy and requires a knowledge of both air and sea temperatures, since differences in the sea temperature of only a few degrees can give rise to, or disperse, fog patches. It is not confined to any particular pressure system since it is only necessary that the air should be flowing over a cold surface. This type of fog is most prevalent in the spring and summer with a south-westerly air stream.

Similar conditions may occur over the land when the surface is covered in snow and ice. Changes in the direction of the tidal stream, especially in an area of numerous shoals, may give a change in the visibility as the underlying cold water is forced to the surface.

Sea fog is liable to form in one area and then drift to another thus bringing about a reduction in the visibility which would not normally have been forecast.

2.   Land fog or radiation fog

This type of fog may be forecast with anticyclonic conditions i.e. clear skies and a light wind at night. A weak pressure gradient is therefore a necessary condition for the formation of land fog. It generally forms during autumn and winter and the late morning in spring. In summer it might form just before sunrise but usually clears shortly afterwards.

Radiation fog will tend to form in valleys and other places where pools of cold air can collect. Ground which is covered in vegetation is more susceptible to this type of fog than towns for example. The formation of a local cloud layer, due possibly to local winds and turbulence, may prevent fog from forming when, with a clear sky, it would have been forecast.

It should be remembered that although this type of fog initially forms over the land it is quite liable to drift out to sea and cover the approaches to harbours and rivers.

The other types of fog are not so easy to forecast and their possibility should be borne in mind when studying the weather map prior to making a forecast. High coastlines may be shrouded in mist or fog, low lying stratus cloud, which may reach down to sea level at times, and can thus bring about a reduction in the visibility.

LOCAL KNOWLEDGE

As has already been mentioned a forecast for a particular area requires a careful study of local effects in relation to the general conditions prevailing. Local knowledge is of great assistance in this respect and the yachtsman is advised to consult the appropriate Admiralty Sailing Directions since these give details of local weather liable to be experienced and any topographical features which may affect some of the above elements more than others.

7

DRAWING A WEATHER MAP

Information relating to the weather may be obtained from the radio, television and press. The most up to date information is that transmitted via the media of radio and television since the weather map and forecasts given in the newspapers, though based on accurate information at the time of going to press, are usually out of date by the time they reach the reader.

The most reliable information is that transmitted by the B.B.C. and since very few boats are likely to have a television set on board the majority of yachtsmen are therefore dependent on the radio as their source of information. Details of the information broadcast by the B.B.C. and G.P.O. Coastal Radio Stations have already been given in the opening chapter of this book and it is the use to which this information can be put that is the subject of this chapter.

The weather forecast for shipping, broadcast by the B.B.C. Radio 2 (formerly Light Programme) is the most useful one for seamen since it gives details of gales, the position and expected movement of the various pressure systems and fronts, along with a forecast for the various sea areas. It also includes up to date information regarding the weather prevailing at certain coastal stations.

The time allocated by the B.B.C. for the transmission of this information is, unfortunately, only five minutes and, as the reader will realise, a lot of relevant information has to be broadcast in this short period. In order to do this the Shipping Forecast has to be read at conversational speed and unless one is proficient in shorthand, and few seafarers are, it is impossible to take the information down direct and it is therefore necessary to resort to some abbreviated, but nevertheless understandable, form.

There are a number of ways in which a weather forecast may be taken down, one of the easiest and most convenient methods being in a tabulated form. In order to do this a certain amount of preparation is necessary since a table is required similar to that shown on page 99. As the forecast is broadcast the relevant information is inserted in the appropriate columns, using abbreviations whenever possible.

The following is an example of a shipping forecast as broadcast by B.B.C. Radio 2 (Light Programme).

"Shipping Forecast at 0640 hours:-

"Gale warnings are in operation in sea areas Forties, Dogger, Fisher and German Bight.

"The general synopsis at midnight last night. A depression of 988 millibars which was positioned at 60° North 10° East is expected to move northeast. A depression of 1004 millibars which was positioned at

98

Weather Forecast   Date: Time:

General Synopsis at   G. M. T.

System	Present Position	Movement	Forecast Position	At

Forecast for Sea Areas

Area	Gales	Wind		Weather	Visibility
		Now	Later		
Viking					
Forties					
Cromarty					
Forth					
Tyne					
Dogger					
Fisher					
German Bight					
Humber					
Thames					
Smith's Knoll					
Dover					
Wight					
Portland					
Plymouth					
Biscay					
Finisterre					
Sole					
Lundy					
Fastnet					
Irish Sea					
Shannon					
Rockall					
Malin					
Hebrides					
Minches					
Fair Isle					
Bailey					
Faeroes					
S. E. Iceland					

Reports from Coastal Stations at   G. M. T.

Station	Wind		Weather	Vis.	Baro.	Tendency
	Dir'n.	Force				
Wick						
Bell Rock						
Dowsing						
Galloper						
Royal Sovereign						
Portland Bill						
Scilly						
Valentia						
Ronaldsway						
Prestwick						
Tiree						

56° North 19° West is expected to move east and to be centred over the south of Scotland by midnight tonight.

"The sea area forecast is as follows:

Viking:-
> Wind northwesterly force 6, becoming northwesterly force 5 to 6. Periods of rain, moderate to good visibility.

Forties:-
> Wind northwesterly force 6 to 8, moderating to northwest force 3 to 5, rain showers, moderate to good visibility.

Cromarty:-
> Wind northwesterly force 3 to 5, veering to southeast force 6, rain, good to moderate visibility.

Dogger, Fisher, German Bight:-
> Wind northwesterly force 6 to 8, moderating to force 4 to 5, periods of rain, good visibility.

Humber, Thames, Dover:-
> Wind westerly force 3 to 5, force 6 in Dover backing southwesterly force 5 to 7 in Thames, rain, good visibility.

Wight, Portland, Plymouth:-
> Wind westerly force 4 to 6, rain turning to drizzle with mist, poor visibility.

Biscay:-
> Wind westerly force 3, cloudy, good visibility.

Finisterre:-
> Wind northeasterly, force 3 to 5, cloudy, good visibility.

Sole, Lundy, Fastnet, Irish Sea, Shannon:-
> Wind southwesterly force 4 to 6, rain at first, drizzle with mist later, good to poor visibility.

Rockall:-
> In the south of the region the wind will be southwesterly force 4 to 6 and in the north, southeasterly force 3 to 5.

Malin:-
> Wind variable force 3 with winds becoming force 5 to 7 at the centre of the low.

Hebrides, Minches:-
> Wind variable, becoming easterly force 3 to 6.

Fair Isle:-
> Wind northerly force 6, becoming easterly force 6, cloudy, good visibility.

Bailey:-
> Wind southeasterly force 5, cloudy, good visibility.

Faeroes:-
> Wind northerly force 3 to 5, becoming easterly force 3 to 5, cloudy, good visibility.

S.E. Iceland:-
> Wind variable force 3, becoming southeasterly force 4 to 6, cloudy, good visibility.

"Coastal reports for 0400 hours:

Wick:-
West force 2, 16 miles, 1016 millibars, rising.

Bell Rock:-
West force 5, cloudy, 22 miles, 1016 millibars, rising slowly.

Dowsing:-
Wind west-north-west force 4, cloudy, 5 miles, 1019 millibars.

Galloper:-
Wind west force 4, 5 miles, 1021 millibars, steady.

Royal Sovereign:-
Wind westerly force 4, 16 miles, 1022 millibars, steady.

Portland Bill:-
Wind west by south force 3, 22 miles, 1022 millibars, falling.

Scilly:-
Wind southwest force 4, light rain during the past hour, 16 miles, 1023 millibars, falling.

Valentia:-
Wind southwest force 4, light rain, 6 miles, 1017 millibars, falling.

Ronaldsway:-
Calm, light rain during the past hour, 9 miles, 1017 millibars, falling.

Prestwick:-
Wind southeasterly force 2, light rain, 13 miles, 1017 millibars, falling.

Tiree:-
Wind east-south-east force 4, 27 miles, 1015 millibars, falling."

The above forecast shows that it would have been a formidable task to take down this information by longhand even if it had been read at dictation speed. Using the prepared table the relevant information should be noted in a similar manner to that explained below and on page 102.

1. In the column marked 'Gales' in the sea area forecast table place a tick against those places where gales are in operation, i.e. Forties, Dogger, Fisher and German Bight.

2. The time of the general synopsis is then given and should be noted, this being followed by information relating to pressure systems which should be entered in the appropriate table using abbreviations similar to those below.

L = low pressure, depression	W = warm front
H = high pressure, anticyclone	C = cold front
T = trough of low pressure	O = occluded front
R = ridge of high pressure	S = secondary front

The pressures given for the various systems are just noted as 988, 1004, the word millibar being omitted since this is understood. Movements are noted as N.E., E; recognised abbreviations for northeast and east respectively.

3. The sea area forecast then follows, the areas being given in the order shown in the table, namely in a clockwise direction around the British Isles.

Where a number of sea areas are grouped together they should be bracketed together as shown.

OUTLOOK

Weather Forecast   Date: 24th May Time: 0640 hrs.
General Synopsis at 0000 G.M.T.

System	Present Position	Movement	Forecast Position	At
L 988	60 N 10 E	NE		
L 1004	56 N 19 W	E	S Scot.	2400

Forecast for Sea Areas

Area	Gales	Wind Now	Wind Later	Weather	Visibility
Viking		NW 6	NW 6/5	p·r	m/g
Forties	✓	NW 6/8	NW 3/5	p·r	m/g
Cromarty		NW 3/5	SE 6	r	g/m
Forth					
Tyne					
Dogger	✓				
Fisher	✓	NW 6/8	NW 4/5	p·r	g
German Bight	✓				
Humber		W 3/5			
Thames			SW 5/7	r	g
Smith's Knoll					
Dover		W 6			
Wight					
Portland		W 4/6		r/d/m	p
Plymouth					
Biscay		W 3		c	g
Finisterre		NE 3/5		c	g
Sole					
Lundy					
Fastnet		SW 4/6		r/d/m	g/p
Irish Sea					
Shannon		SW 4/6 (S)			
Rockall		SE 3/5 (N)			
Malin		Var 3	5/7 at centre of L.		
Hebrides		Var	E 3/6	c	g
Minches					
Fair Isle		N 6	E 6	c	g
Bailey		SE 5		c	g
Faeroes		N 3/5	E 3/5	c	g
S.E. Iceland		Var 3	SE 4/6	c	g

Reports from Coastal Stations at 0400 hrs. G.M.T.

Station	Wind Dir'n.	Wind Force	Weather	Vis.	Baro.	Tendency
Wick	W	2		16	1016	/
Bell Rock	W	5	c	22	1016	/
Dowsing	WNW	4	c	5	1019	
Galloper	W	4		5	1021	—
Royal Sovereign	W	4		16	1022	—
Portland Bill	WxS	3		22	1022	\
Scilly	SW	4	r	16	1023	\
Valentia	SW	4	r	6	1017	\
Ronaldsway	Calm		r	9	1017	\
Prestwick	SE	2	r	13	1017	\
Tiree	ESE	4		27	1015	\

The column marked 'gales' has already been ticked off as described in (1) above.

The column marked 'wind' should cause no difficulty, entering the direction and force directly in the appropriate columns. A decrease or increase in the force being indicated by a vertical stroke i.e. north-west force 6 to 4 being noted as N.W. 6/4.

The column marked 'weather' is then filled in using various abbreviations to indicate rain, snow, etc., and in this respect the Beaufort notation for the weather will be very convenient.

Weather	Beaufort Letter	Weather	Beaufort Letter
Blue sky	b	Overcast sky	o
Partly cloudy sky	bc	Squally weather	q
Cloudy	c	Rain	r
Drizzle	d	Sleet	rs
Fog	f	Snow	s
Gale	g	Thunder	t
Hail	h	Thunderstorm	tlr
Lightning	l	Dust haze	z
Mist	m		

The prefix 'p' may be used to denote 'showers of' e.g. pr = showers of rain. Capital letters may be used to denote intensity, thus R = heavy rain. Letters repeated denote continuity, thus RR = continuous heavy rain. The prefix 'i' denotes 'intermittent', thus ir = intermittent rain. A solidus, vertical line, may be used to divide the present weather from that expected in the future, thus r/d/m = rain followed by drizzle then mist.

The advantage with the above notation is that in the majority of cases the initial letter of the word corresponds to the Beaufort letter.

Instead of the Beaufort letter a symbol may be used to denote the weather. These are not so convenient to use unless one is familiar with them. They may be found convenient for showing the weather to be expected in the various sea areas after drawing the weather map, and will be recognised as those used on the weather forecast chart shown on B.B.C. television.

Symbols:

Weather	Symbol	Weather	Symbol
Mist	═	Rain shower	▽̇
Fog	≡	Rain and snow shower	▽
Drizzle	୨		
Rain	•	Snow shower	▽
Rain and snow	✷̇	Hail shower	▽
Snow	✳	Thunderstorm	☒

The column marked visibility is filled in using the following abbreviations:

f = fog
p = poor
m = moderate
g = good
vg = very good

4. The reports from the various coastal stations are now entered in the appropriate columns in a similar manner to that used for the various sea areas. The word 'miles' or even the abbreviation 'm' need not be inserted in the visibility column and only the last two numbers of the pressure need be entered since no confusion should arise as to whether a 10 or 9 precedes them. The pressure tendencies may be indicated by a straight line sloping up or down from left to right. A rising pressure would be shown by⟋, a steady pressure —, and a falling pressure⟍.
   The angle that this sloping line makes with the horizontal can be used as an indication of the rate at which the pressure is rising or falling, the steeper the slope the greater the tendency.

CONSTRUCTING A WEATHER MAP

The above information should now be plotted on the map or chart of the area and a start made with the drawing of the weather map.

The position of the various pressure systems should be plotted for the time stated in the forecast. It is only necessary to insert the word 'Low' or 'High' in the position given, with the pressure at the centre of the 'low' or 'high' being inserted just above or below. Plot the future position and, or, movement of these systems and draw in lightly any fronts that may have been given in the general synopsis, see figure 84.

Use is now made of a 'station model' to plot the winds, pressure if given, and weather at each of the coastal stations and at the centre of each sea area. Figure 83 shows a 'station model' and the method to be used in plotting the corresponding information. The centre of the small circle denotes the centre of the coastal station or sea area and either the Beaufort notation or symbols should be used for depicting the weather. An expected shift in the wind direction is shown by drawing a small arrow between the two wind arrows, as shown, this arrow being in the direction of the expected shift. The feathers on the arrows are always drawn on the side of the lowest pressure, namely on the left hand side in the northern hemisphere when flying with the wind. One large feather is used to represent a wind of force 2 and half a feather as a wind of force 1.

Figure 84 shows the first stage in the drawing of a weather map where the pressure systems and prevailing winds, pressure and weather have been plotted at the various coastal stations and for the various sea areas.

The most recent information reported in the shipping forecast regarding actual winds, pressure and the prevailing weather is that given by the coastal stations for 0400 hours and it is for this time that the weather map should be drawn. Since the forecast was received at approximately 0640 hours the final weather map showing the pressure distribution and prevailing winds will be only a few hours out of date by the time that it is completed.

At first sight the amount of information received appears rather scanty for the drawing of a weather map but if the following procedure is used, plus the fact that the final weather map will tend towards a pattern similar to that of one of the examples shown in the preceding chapters, a fairly reasonable map can be drawn.

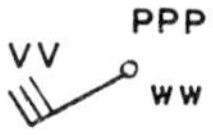

where,

    o   =   centre of station or sea area
    PPP   =   pressure in millibars
    VV   =   visibility
    ww   =   weather
    arrow =   direction and force of the wind

example:

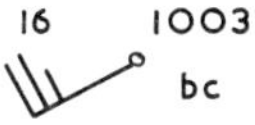

pressure 1003 mbs., visibility 16 miles,
partly cloudy weather, wind S.W., force 5

example:

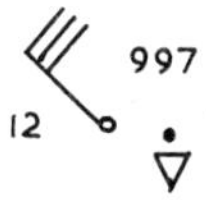

pressure 997 mbs., visibility 12 miles,
rain showers, wind N.W. force 6

example:

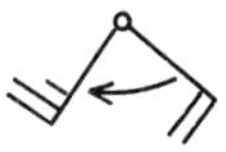

wind S.E. force 4 becoming S.W. force 5

Figure 83

The positions of the pressure systems, as given for midnight last night and for the period twenty four hours later, having already been plotted it is now necessary to interpolate between the two positions to arrive at the position for 0400 hours.

In figure 85 the centre of the 'low' 1004 mbs., is shown in position 56° N 19° W for midnight last night and in its expected position twenty four hours later to the south of Scotland. In four hours, from midnight to 0400 hours, it will have moved approximately one sixth of the distance between these two positions and will be at the position shown. Likewise the 'low' 988 mbs., over Scandinavia is shown to have had a slight north-easterly movement during this four hour period.

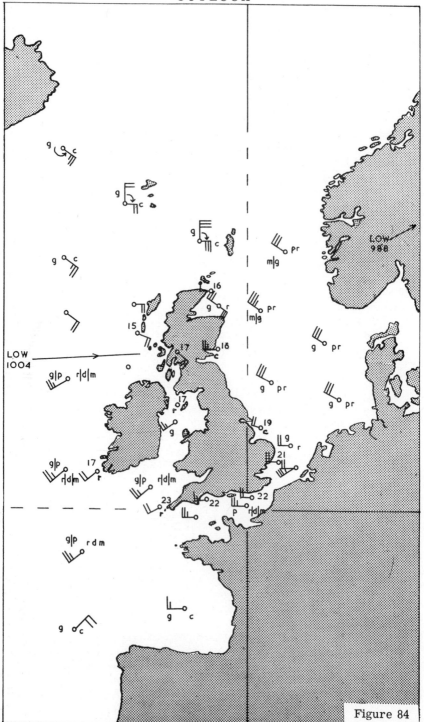

Figure 84

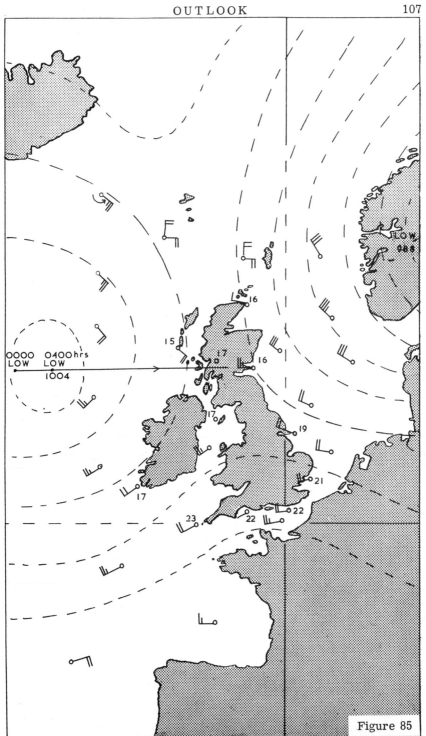

Figure 85

The isobars should now be drawn in and it is suggested that they are drawn at intervals of 4 mbs., the isobar for 1000 mbs. always being shown.

Select the lowest or highest pressure and commence by drawing an isobar around this area. Isobars should never cross each other, touch or join, except in the latter case where they complete a curve around the central high or low. Pressures should always be higher on one side and lower on the other side along the same isobar. The pressure between consecutive isobars must always differ by the same amount except at a col.

When drawing the isobars they should, as far as possible, fit the wind direction bearing in mind that there is usually an angle of indraught towards the lower pressure, this angle being less over the sea than over the land. If in doubt draw the isobars parallel to the wind direction since no great error should occur.

Buys Ballot's Law can be used to advantage in this respect, it states:

"If the observer stands with his back to the wind, the lower pressure will be on his left if in the northern hemisphere and on his right if in the southern hemisphere".

Seamen, in general, prefer to face the wind and the law is then:

"Face the wind; the lower pressure will lie to the right if in the northern hemisphere and to the left if in the southern hemisphere".

The spacing of the isobars corresponds to the wind strength, the steeper the gradient the stronger the wind and the closer the isobars. Likewise a weak gradient and light winds indicate that the isobars are widely spaced. When the distance between the pressures reported at the coastal stations and the centres of low (or high) pressure are well apart, then the distance between the reports should be divided uniformly unless the wind strengths vary considerably over the area. In the latter case there should be a gradual transition from one area to another, rather than a concentration of isobars in one area and a scarcity in another area.

In figure 85, the low over Scandinavia has a pressure of 988 mbs. and the nearest report is 1016 mbs. at Wick. Divide the distance between the two positions uniformly remembering that the isobars are to be drawn at 4 mbs. intervals and that the isobar of 1000 mbs. must be included. Six isobars have therefore to be inserted between the isobar of 1016 mbs. and 988 mbs. namely 1012, 1008, 1004, 1000, 996, 992 mbs. Notice that the pressure at Bell Rock is also 1016 mbs. and therefore the 1016 mbs. isobar should be drawn to pass through both Wick and Bell Rock.

On the same principle isobars should be inserted around the low of 1004 mbs. The nearest pressures to this low are at Tiree, 1015 mbs., and Valentia, 1017 mbs. The isobar of 1016 mbs. will therefore be drawn slightly to the east of Tiree and to the west of Valentia as shown.

Full use must be made of the station reports for both pressure and wind when sketching in the isobars.

Draw the isobars in lightly at first and when completed examine the weather map to see whether the general pressure distribution and future movements correspond to the forecasted winds for the various sea areas.

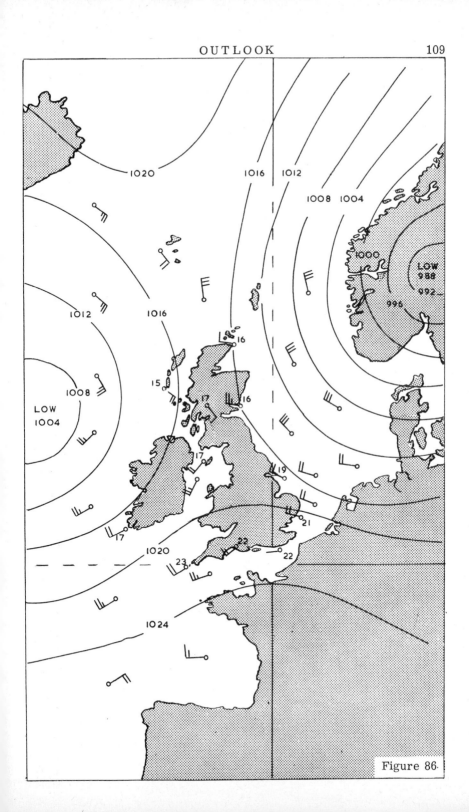

Figure 86.

In figure 85, a col appears to be situated over Scotland at 0400 hours. This was initially to the west of Scotland as indicated by the light variable winds in S.E. Iceland and the Hebrides. The shift of wind direction, as given in the shipping forecast, corresponds to that expected from the weather map. At present the wind in Cromarty is from the northwest and, with the passage of the col to the east, will back to the southeast. Westerly winds at present being experienced in Thames will back to the southwest with the passage of the weak ridge of high pressure over southern England.

Figure 86 shows the completed weather map for 0400 hours; for clarity the future changes in the wind directions have been omitted.

Summarising, the sequence of plotting is as follows:-

1. Plot the centres of low and high pressure.
2. Mark in the future movements of these centres.
3. Insert fronts, if any, as accurately as possible.
4. Sketch in the isobars starting where the winds are strongest by taking the lowest pressure reported.

A general forecast for the British Isles would probably read as follows:

"Rain, heavy in places, will affect all areas during the day although the north of Scotland will be dry at first. Brighter and mainly dry weather will soon reach northern Ireland and extend east to most places by the evening."

Forecasts for the various sea areas are as already given in the shipping forecast.

The following examples show the weather maps associated with particular shipping forecasts. Since the reader would, in all probability, take down the forecast in a tabulated form it has been presented here in that manner.

It is suggested that the reader takes each shipping forecast and then draws his own weather map, comparing the finished result with that shown here.

In each example two maps have been drawn for clarity. The first map shows the position of the pressure systems and associated fronts for the time of the general synopsis, their movements, predicted positions twenty four hours later and their interpolated positions for the time of the coastal station reports. The second map shows the complete pressure distribution and prevailing winds for this latter time.

EXAMPLE 14   Weather Forecast   Date: 4ᵗʰ June   Time: 0640 hrs.
General Synopsis at 0000 hrs. G. M. T.

System	Present Position	Movement	Forecast Position	At
L 996	57N 22W	E	North Sea	2400
W	SW. Br. Is.	E	clear N Sea.	"
T	NE Scot, N.Sea	E	" " "	"
L 1000	Scandinavia	E		

Forecast for Sea Areas

Area	Gales	Wind Now	Wind Later	Weather	Visibility
Viking	}	SE3		c	m
Forties	}				
Cromarty		SE3	N2	/f	m/p
Forth		E2	W2.	pr	m/p
Tyne		SW2.	NW3	d	p/m
Dogger	}				
Fisher	}	SE2	Var		p
German Bight	}				
Humber	}				
Thames	}	S2	WSW4	pr	m
Smith's Knoll	}				
Dover	}				
Wight	}				
Portland	}	SW3	W3	pr	m
Plymouth	}				
Biscay		W2			g
Finisterre	}	NW2			g
Sole	}				
Lundy	}	SW2.	NW4		m/g.
Fastnet					
Irish Sea					
Shannon		SW4/5	NW3/2		g
Rockall	}	SW4/3	NW4/5		m/g
Malin					
Hebrides	}	S4	NW2		m/g.
Minches	}				
Fair Isle		SE2.	NE2	/f	m/p
Bailey		SE3	NW4		m
Faeroes		SE3	NE4		m
S.E.Iceland		SE2	NE3		m/g.

Reports from Coastal Stations at 0400 hrs. G. M. T.

Station	Wind Dir'n.	Wind Force	Weather	Vis.	Baro.	Tendency
Wick	ESE	3	m	2	1010	⌐
Bell Rock	SSW	3	d	4	1010	⌐
Dowsing	SW	3		8	1015	⌐
Galloper	SW	2.	d	4	1019	—
Royal Sovereign	SW	2		12	1020	—
Portland Bill	SW	2	⌐	8	1019	/
Scilly	SW	5	⌐	4	1021	⌐
Valentia	SW	5	d	5	1015	⌐
Ronaldsway	SSW	2.	⌐	7	1012	⌐
Prestwick	SSW	2		14	1010	⌐
Tiree	S	4	d	5	1008	⌐/

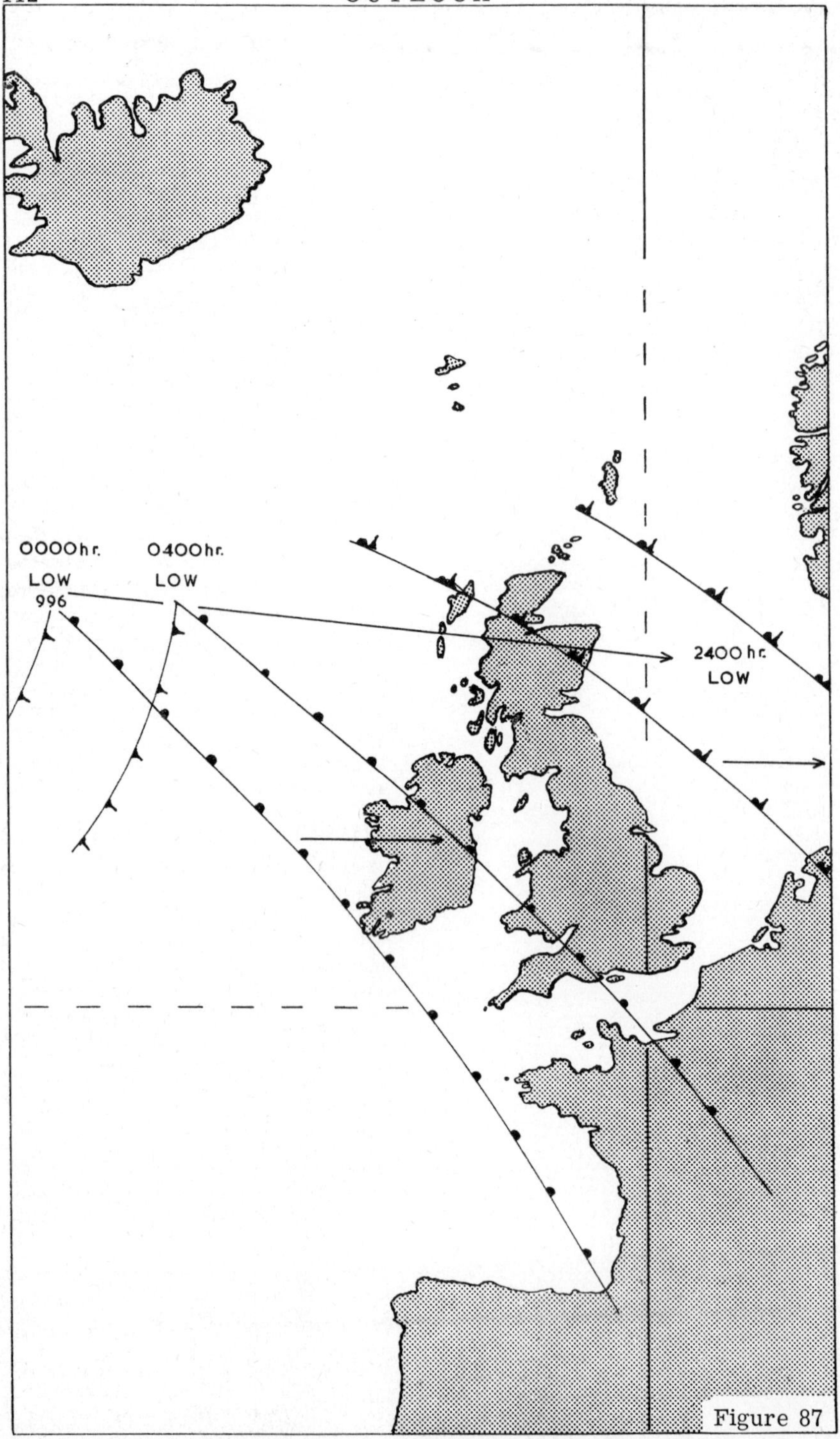

Figure 87

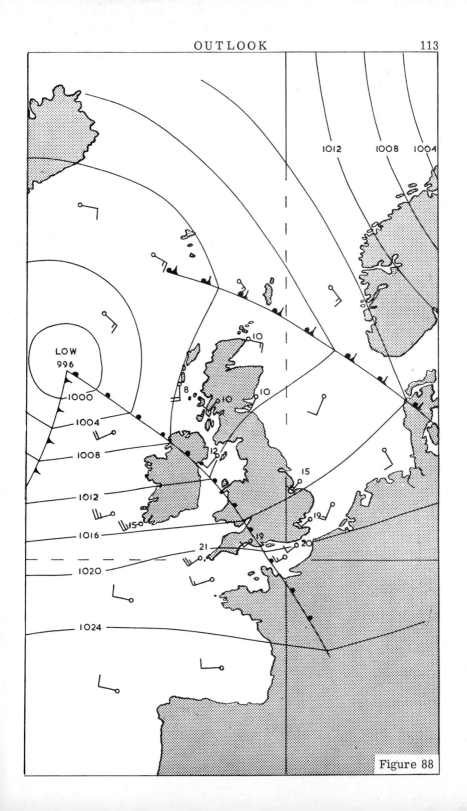

Figure 88

The general synopsis shows a depression to the west of Scotland approaching the British Isles with its associated warm front extending in a southeasterly direction to the southwest of Ireland and England. A trough of low pressure, an occluded front, lies in a northwest to southeast direction to the northeast of Scotland. See figures 87 and 88.

The major depression is not very deep, 996 mbs., this being substantiated by the prevailing winds in the adjacent sea areas which do not exceed force 5.

The occluded trough still appears to be active as shown by the marked change in the wind direction before and in the rear of the front. This shift in the wind direction is of great assistance when drawing in the isobars, there being a marked change along the front.

Light winds in the North Sea indicate a weak pressure gradient and widely spaced isobars in this area whereas nearer to the centre of the depression, to the west of Ireland, winds are much stronger indicating a steeper gradient and closely spaced isobars.

A general forecast for the British Isles would be as follows:

"It will be cloudy with rain in all parts of the British Isles at first. Brighter drier weather will reach Northern Ireland by the afternoon extending slowly eastwards to all districts. There will, however, be some showers, chiefly in the north and east."

EXAMPLE 15

Weather Forecast   Date: 27th July   Time: 1355 hrs.

General Synopsis at 0600 hrs G.M.T.

System	Present Position	Movement	Forecast Position	At
L 998	S W Iceland.	ESE	Faeroes	0600.
T	N. Atl.	E	Scot / W. Ire.	
R.	Scot / Ire.	E	N. Sea	

Forecast for Sea Areas

Area	Gales	Wind		Weather	Visibility
		Now	Later		
Viking	}	NW3	SE2		g
Forties					
Cromarty		NW2	S2.	c/r	g/m
Forth	}	NW2	SW3	c/r	g/m
Tyne					
Dogger		N3	SW3		g
Fisher		NW3			g
German Bight		NW3	W2.		g
Humber		N3	W2.	c/r	m
Thames		NW2	SW2		g
Smith's Knoll					
Dover	}	W2.	SW2		g
Wight					
Portland		NW2	Calm		g
Plymouth	}				
Biscay		N 1/2.	Calm		g
Finisterre	}				
Sole		Calm	W2.		g
Lundy	}	N3	Sw2		g
Fastnet					
Irish Sea		NNW3	SW4	r	m.
Shannon		Var 1/2	SW 3/4	r	g/m.
Rockall		SW 2/3	NW4	pr	m
Malin		N2	W3/4	pr	m
Hebrides	}	NW2		pr	m
Minches					
Fair Isle		NW2	SW4	r	g/m.
Bailey		SW2	NW3/4	r	g/m.
Faeroes		SW2.	Var	/r	g/m.
S. E. Iceland		SW3	NE3	r/	m/g.

Reports from Coastal Stations at 1200 hrs. G.M.T.

Station	Wind		Weather	Vis.	Baro.	Tendency
	Dir'n.	Force				
Wick	WNW	3		36	1015	/
Bell Rock	NW	2.		32	1016	/
Dowsing	N	2		25	1016	/
Galloper	N	2.		23	1015	/
Royal Sovereign	NNE	3		18	1016	/
Portland Bill	NNE	3		18	1018	/
Scilly	N	2.		19	1022	/
Valentia	NW	2.		24	1023	/
Ronaldsway	SE	2.		37	1020	/
Prestwick	W	3		35	1019	/
Tiree	WSW	4		35.	1018	/

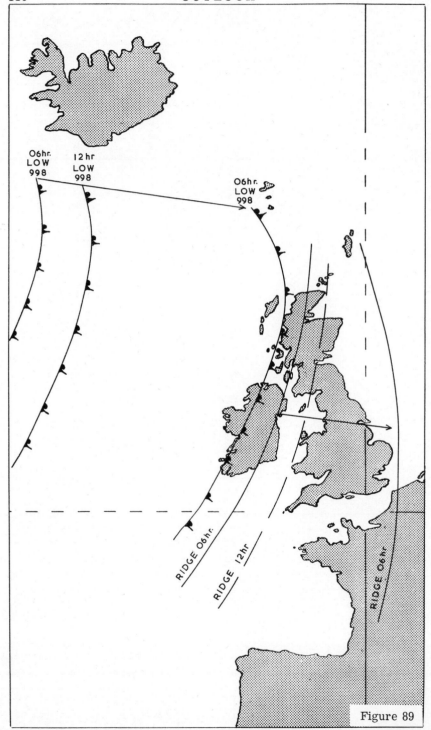

Figure 89

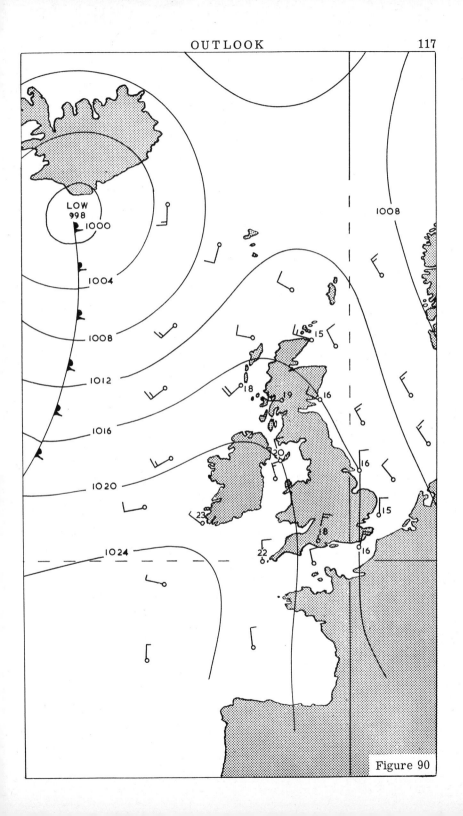

Figure 90

The general synopsis shows a shallow depression to the southwest of Iceland with its associated trough of low pressure to the west of the British Isles. The dominating pressure system over the British Isles is the ridge of high pressure over Scotland and Ireland, figures 89, 90.

Although it has not been mentioned in the general synopsis, pressure would appear to be low over Scandinavia. When drawing in the isobars the forecasted winds must be used as a guide, the lighter the winds the weaker the pressure gradient and the further apart will the isobars be drawn.

A general forecast for the next twenty four hours would be as follows:

"It will be generally dry with sunny periods. Cloudy weather with rain will move into northwestern areas during the night and will reach all areas except possibly the south of England within the next twenty four hours. Bright showery weather will follow the rain belt over northwestern areas."

OUTLOOK

EXAMPLE 16

Weather Forecast   Date: 29th April Time: 0640 hrs.

General Synopsis at 0000 hrs. G.M.T.

System	Present Position	Movement	Forecast Position	At
L 986	W Scot	E	N. North Sea	2400hrs.
W	E to S.Scand.	NE	clear " "	
C	Irish S to Finisterre	NE	" " "	

Forecast for Sea Areas

Area	Gales	Wind		Weather	Visibility
		Now	Later		
Viking		SSE3	S4	r	P
Forties		S4	SW4	r	P
Cromarty					
Forth		SW4	NW6/7	r	m/g.
Tyne					
Dogger		SW3/4	WSW6/7	pr	m
Fisher		SSE3	SW5/6	f/d.	P
German Bight		SW2	SW6/7	m/pr	p/m
Humber		SW2.	WSW6	m/pr	p/m
Thames					
Smith's Knoll		S2	SW5	m/c	P/g
Dover					
Wight					
Portland		SSW2	W4	m/c	P/g.
Plymouth		SW2	W2	d	P
Biscay		W3	NW1/2	r	m
Finisterre		NW4	N2		g
Sole		NW3			g
Lundy		W4	NW2/3	r	m
Fastnet					
Irish Sea		WSW4	W6	r	m
Shannon		NW4	W3	pr	g
Rockall		N4/5	NW3	pr	g
Malin		Var4	NNW6	r	m
Hebrides		NE5	NW5/6	pr	m/g
Minches		NE3/4	N5		g
Fair Isle		E4	NE3	r/d	m/p
Bailey		NW3/4	Var		m
Faeroes		NE2	NE4		m/g
S.E.Iceland		Calm		c	m/g

Reports from Coastal Stations at 0400 hrs G.M.T.

Station	Wind		Weather	Vis.	Baro.	Tendency
	Dir'n.	Force				
Wick	SE	4	r	13	996	\
Bell Rock	S	4	pr	3	997	\
Dowsing	SW	4	m	2	1005	\
Galloper	SW	3	m	2	1009	\
Royal Sovereign	WSW	3	pr	8	1009	—
Portland Bill	SW	3	pr	11	1008	/
Scilly	W	4	pr	13	1008	/
Valentia	W	4	pr	15	1004	/
Ronaldsway	SW	5	c	13	998	\
Prestwick	S	5/6	pr	5	996	\
Tiree	SW	4		19	988	\

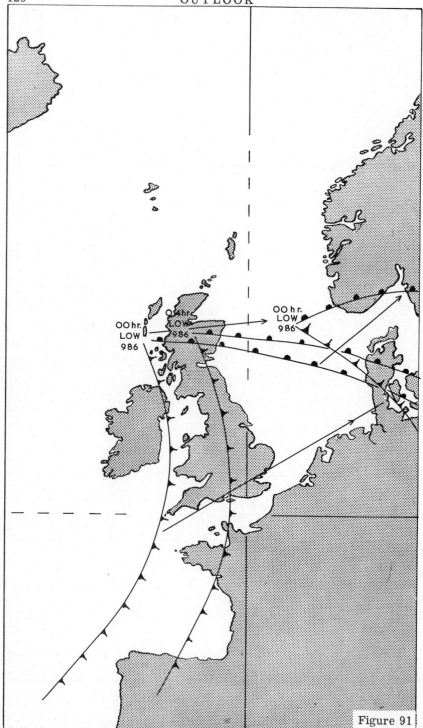

Figure 91

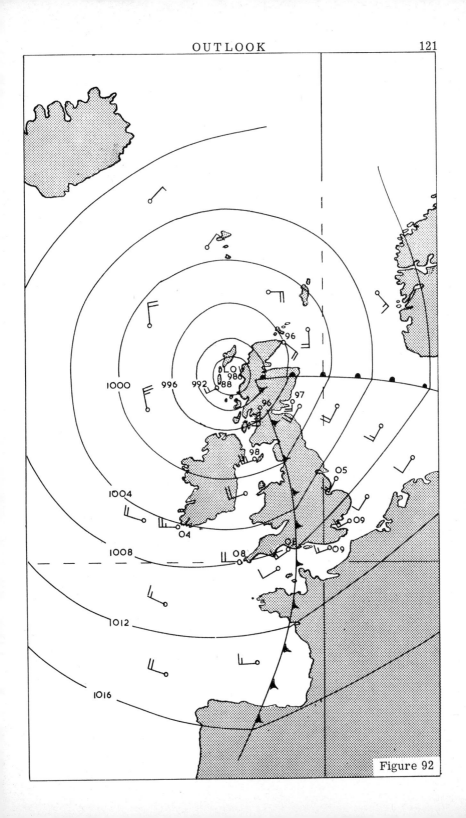

Figure 92

The general synopsis shows a deep depression, 986 mbs., to the west of Scotland with a warm front extending east across the northern part of the North Sea to the south of Scandinavia. The cold front lies in a north to south direction through the Irish Sea to Finisterre, figures 91 & 92.

The isobars in the warm sector, the area between the warm and cold fronts, are drawn more or less straight and there are sufficient pressure reports from coastal stations on the east coast of the British Isles to give guidance regarding their direction. The direction of the prevailing wind will also be a help in this respect.

Light winds and calms in S. E. Iceland and adjacent sea areas indicate widely spaced isobars in these areas. Notice how the wind strengths are expected to increase with the passage of the cold front as shown by the wind arrows for 'winds later' in the areas at present covered by the warm sector.

A general forecast for the next twenty four hours would be as follows:

"Scotland will remain cloudy with rain for much of the time although brighter weather will spread into western districts later. Over the rest of the area it will be cloudy at first with rain but as this belt of rain moves to the east it will be followed by clear periods with scattered showers."

EXAMPLE 17 Weather Forecast Date: 15ᵗʰ Nov. Time: 1355 hrs

General Synopsis at 0600hrs G. M. T.

System	Present Position	Movement	Forecast Position	At
L 969	200m SE Iceland	SE	Centre Fair Isle	0600
H	Greenland, Azores			

Forecast for Sea Areas

Area	Gales	Wind Now	Wind Later	Weather	Visibility
Viking	✓	SW 8/9	Cyc 7/9	P	g
Forties	✓				
Cromarty	✓				
Forth	✓	W 7/9		P	g
Tyne	✓				
Dogger	✓				
Fisher	✓				
German Bight	✓				
Humber	✓	SW-W 6/8	W 8/10	R	g
Thames	✓				
Smith's Knoll	✓				
Dover	✓				
Wight	✓				
Portland	✓	W 6/8	W 7/9	R	g
Plymouth	✓				
Biscay		NWxN 3/4	W 4/6	r	g
Finisterre	(S)	E 3	Var	c	g
Sole	✓	W/NW 7		P	g
Lundy	✓	SW-W 7/8	W-NW	P	g
Fastnet	✓		8/10		
Irish Sea	✓	SW-W 8/9	W-NW 9/10	P	g
Shannon	✓	NW 8/10	NW 7/9	P	g
Rockall	✓				
Malin	✓	NW 9/10	NW-N 9	P	g
Hebrides	✓				
Minches	✓				
Fair Isle	✓	SW-S 7/9	N 7/9	P	g
Bailey	✓	NW 9/10	NW-N 9	P	g
Faeroes	✓	NW 8/10	N 8	P	g
S.E. Iceland	✓	N 8/10		P	g

Reports from Coastal Stations at 1000 hrs G. M. T.

Station	Wind Dir'n.	Wind Force	Weather	Vis.	Baro.	Tendency
Wick	SWxW	5		22	990	⌐
Bell Rock	WSW	6		16	997	—
Dowsing	SWxS	6		5	1012	
Galloper	WSW	6		5	1016	—
Royal Sovereign	W	6		11	1018	
Portland Bill	WxS	7	r	16	1018	⌐
Scilly	WxN	6	d	5	1022	—
Valentia	WNW	6	r	9	1019	／
Ronaldsway						
Prestwick						
Tiree						

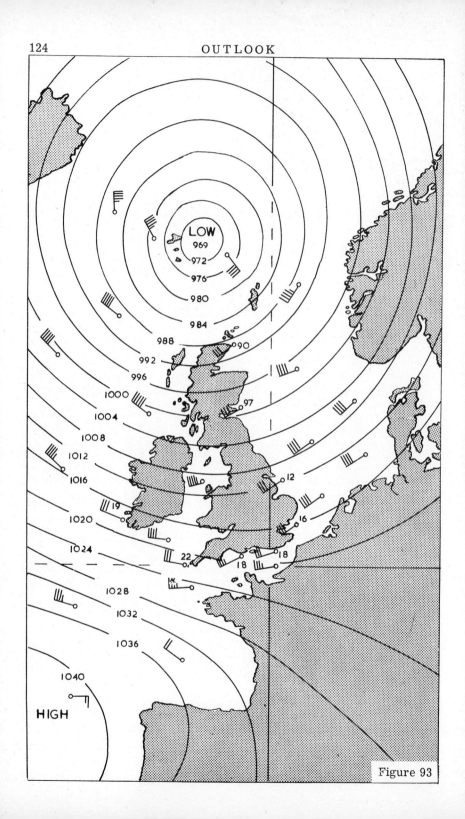

LOW
969
972
976
980
984
988
992
996
1000
1004
1008
1012
1016
1020
1024
1028
1032
1036
1040
HIGH

Figure 93

The general synopsis shows a very deep depression to the southeast of Iceland to be the predominating pressure system covering the area. This depression is slow moving as is shown by the forecast position for 0600 hrs, 16th November. Pressure is high to the west over Greenland and to the southwest in the vicinity of the Azores.

The gale force winds being experienced round the coasts of the British Isles and in the adjacent sea areas indicate a very steep pressure gradient. The isobars should therefore be spaced closely together and, since the system is cyclonic, circular in shape. Figure 93 shows the pressure distribution and prevailing winds for 1000 hours.

A general forecast for the next twenty four hours would be as follows:

"The very strong westerly airstream will persist with gale force winds in all areas, severe in Scotland and northern England. There will be blustery showers in all areas with some clear or sunny intervals. The showers may be of snow over high ground in Scotland and there will also be hail and thunderstorms."

The outlook for a further twenty four hours is:

"Cold, showery weather with the winds slowly moderating."

In the above example only one weather map has been drawn since the movement during the next 24 hours, as given in the general synopsis, is very small.

The Royal Meteorological Society publish pads of Metmaps to facilitate the taking down of the shipping forecast and the drawing of weather maps.

At the back of this book the reader will find two tables and two charts for his own use in taking down and subsequent plotting of a weather forecast.

8

STORM SIGNALS

Gale warnings are transmitted by the B.B.C. and certain G.P.O. coastal radio stations as mentioned previously on page 6. In addition to these broadcasts certain coastal signal stations around the coast of the British Isles display storm signals on the receipt of a gale warning. These visual signals indicate that a gale is expected within the next 12 hours, or is already in progress, in the coastal area within which the signal station is situated.

A list of these signal stations will be found in the No. 1 Weekly Edition of Admiralty Notices to Mariners, Reed's Nautical Almanac and other publications.

The storm warning consists of hoisting a black painted cone, 3 feet high and 3 feet wide at the base, by day or a triangle of white or red lights at night, see figure 94.

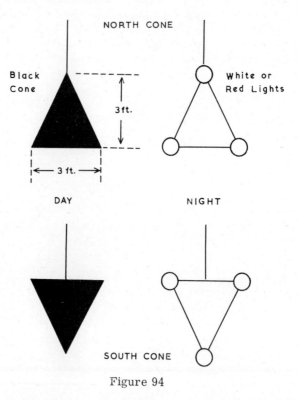

Figure 94

NORTH CONE

When gales are expected from any point north of the east to west line a cone is hoisted point upwards by day or the triangle of lights apex upwards by night.

SOUTH CONE

When gales are expected from any point south of the east to west line a cone is hoisted point downwards by day or the triangle of lights apex downwards by night.

When the direction of the gale is expected to change from the northern side to the southern side of the east-west line, the north cone is lowered and the south cone hoisted. Conversely, when the direction of the gale is expected to change from the southern side to the northern side of the east-west line the cone is changed accordingly. Southwesterly gales veering to the northwest would be shown initially by the hoisting of the south cone and this would then be replaced by the north cone at the time that they were expected to veer to the northwest.

The signal will be lowered when the wind drops to below gale force provided that a renewal of the gale force winds is not expected within six hours. The signal will remain hoisted during a temporary lull in the gale force winds.

Inshore yachtsmen, for whose benefit these visual gale warnings are primarily intended, are advised that the cone signal relates solely to the operation of a local sea area gale warning. These visual warnings are to be regarded only as supplementary to the more detailed weather bulletins for shipping which are regularly broadcast by the B.B.C. and G. P.O. coastal radio stations.

METEOROLOGICAL EFFECTS ON TIDES AND TIDAL STREAMS

The prevailing winds and pressure systems may have a considerable effect on the height of tides and the rate of tidal streams.

The sea level is liable to be raised in the direction towards which the wind is blowing and to be lowered in the direction from which it is blowing.

A depression, a low barometer, tends to raise the sea level whereas an anticyclone, a high barometer, tends to lower the sea level.

In the North Sea meteorological conditions have a considerable effect upon the sea level, especially in the southern part. Tides which rise or fall 2 to 3 feet above or below the predicted heights of high or low water are not uncommon. Generally, northerly winds raise the sea level by driving water southwards into the relatively narrow part of the North Sea and to a lesser extent southerly winds remove the water from this area.

Other areas are likewise affected around the coast and reference should be made to the appropriate 'Sailing Directions'.

Storm surges occasionally occur which cause a sudden rise in the sea level. An instance of this occurring is when a depression travels quickly across the northern part of the North Sea. The rapid changes in the wind circulation set up oscillations in the sea level to a greater extent than that which can be solely attributed to the wind strengths.

Prolonged droughts or floods affecting the upper reaches will possibly affect the tidal predictions for harbours situated in estuaries or rivers.

Sudden changes in meteorological conditions, for instance the passage of a line squall, may set up non-tidal fluctuations in the water level. These are referred to as 'seiches' and may give rise to waves from only a few inches up to several feet in height with a period between the waves of from a few minutes up to a few hours. The effect is similar to that which takes place in shallow water when a large vessel goes by.

Changes in the height of the tide also affect the horizontal movement of the water, namely tidal streams. Unless the meteorological effects are prolonged the effect on the tidal streams seldom exceeds 1 knot.

The seaman should bear in mind that a wind blowing against a strong tide is likely to give rise to an uncomfortable short steep sea.

9

WEATHER LORE

There are a number of sayings or rhymes which relate to the weather and which could be used in forecasting. A forecast based on these sayings should be treated with caution and relied on only for relatively short periods of time.

A number of these sayings refer to the scattering effect of particles in the atmsophere on the sun's rays, others on the fact that the weather of the British Isles travels generally in a west to east direction.

The white light of the sun is made up of all the colours of the rainbow and under certain circumstances some of these colours are scattered to a greater extent than others. Minute dust particles in the atmosphere cause the blue, green and yellow rays to be scattered to a greater extent than the red rays so that only these latter rays reach the observer and under such conditions the sun and sky appear red in colour. Water droplets, being very much larger than these dust particles, have a greatly reduced effect on the sun's rays so that the sun appears white. The sun shining through fog often appears as a white disc.

The saying,

"A red sky at night is a sailor's delight,
A red sky in the morning is a sailorman's warning."

is an example of the above effect.

A red sky at sunset indicates a relatively dry atmosphere to the west, the presence of dust particles, and since the weather generally moves from west to east it is an indication of the approach of fine weather. A dull grey or white colour at sunset would be an indication of water droplets in the atmosphere and the probability of wet weather to follow.

A red sky in the morning is usually caused by high cloud, pre-warm front cloud, being illuminated from below and thus indicating the approach of bad weather from the west. A grey sky at this time would indicate the presence of water droplets in the atmosphere to the east and the passage of the bad weather.

The saying,

"The evening red and morning grey
Are sure signs of a fine day,
But the evening grey and the morning red,
Makes the sailor shake his head."

is another example describing the above conditions.

Some of the sayings refer to the direction of the wind and the type of weather that such a wind brings with it.

The saying,

> "When the rain comes from the east
> It will rain for twenty four hours at least."

is an indication of a depression to the south of the British Isles which is slow moving or remaining stationary over France. The observer is then in the area to the north of the centre and long periods of rain may be expected.

East and northeast winds bring air off the continent. These are bitterly cold and dry in winter, warm and very dry in summer, hence the saying,

> "When the wind is in the east
> 'Tis neither good for man nor beast."

Good visibility is often experienced in the polar air before a warm front, to be followed by rain and poor visibility in the warm sector, hence the saying.

> "The farther the sight, the nearer the rain."

A few sayings relate to the barometer as the following example shows:

> "Long foretold, long last,
> Short notice, soon past.
> Quick rise after low,
> Sure sign of stronger blow."

A slowly falling barometer is an indication of a prolonged spell of bad weather since the depression associated with the falling barometer covers a large area. A quick fall followed by a quick rise indicates the passage of a trough and as would be expected under such conditions the winds are usually very much stronger in the rear of the trough line than before it.

The following sayings or rhymes refer to the wind, weather and barometer and although there is a certain amount of truth in them they should be treated with caution.

1.   Mackerel sky and mare's tails,
   Make lofty ships carry low sails.

2.   When the wind shifts against the sun
   Trust it not, for back it will run.

3.   When the rain comes before the wind,
   Halyards, sheets and braces mind,
   But when the wind comes before the rain,
   Soon you may make sail again.

4.   If clouds are gathering thick and fast,
   Keep sharp lookout for sail and mast,
   But if they slowly onward crawl
   Shoot your lines, nets and trawl.

5.   When the glass falls low
      Prepare for a blow;
      When it slowly rises high,
      Lofty canvas you may fly.

6.   At sea with low and falling glass,
      Soundly sleeps a careless ass,
      Only when it's high and rising,
      Truly rests a careful wise one.

7.   Evening red and morning grey
      Help the traveller on his way.
      Evening grey and morning red
      Bring down rain upon his head.

8.   Mackerel sky, mackerel sky, never long wet,
      and never long dry.

9.   Mackerel sky, fair today, wet tomorrow.

10.   When the wind is in the East
      'Tis neither good for man nor beast;
      When the wind is in the North
      The skilful fisher goes not forth;
      When the wind is in the South
      It blows the bait in the fish's mouth;
      When the wind is in the West
      Then 'tis at the very best.

11.   The south wind always brings wet weather,
      The north wind wet and cold together;
      The west wind always brings us rain,
      The east wind blows it back again.

12.   If the sun in red should set,
      The next day surely will be wet;
      If the sun should set in grey,
      The next will be a rainy day.

13.   Dirty days hath September,
      April, June and November;
      From January up to May
      The rain it raineth every day.
      All the rest have thirty one,
      Without a blessed gleam of sun,
      And if any of them had two-and-thirty
      They'd be just as wet and twice as dirty!

OUTLOOK

Weather Forecast   Date: Time:

General Synopsis at   G. M. T.

System	Present Position	Movement	Forecast Position	At

Forecast for Sea Areas

Area	Gales	Wind Now	Wind Later	Weather	Visibility
Viking					
Forties					
Cromarty					
Forth					
Tyne					
Dogger					
Fisher					
German Bight					
Humber					
Thames					
Smith's Knoll					
Dover					
Wight					
Portland					
Plymouth					
Biscay					
Finisterre					
Sole					
Lundy					
Fastnet					
Irish Sea					
Shannon					
Rockall					
Malin					
Hebrides					
Minches					
Fair Isle					
Bailey					
Faeroes					
S. E. Iceland					

Reports from Coastal Stations at   G. M. T.

Station	Wind Dir'n.	Wind Force	Weather	Vis.	Baro.	Tendency
Wick						
Bell Rock						
Dowsing						
Galloper						
Royal Sovereign						
Portland Bill						
Scilly						
Valentia						
Ronaldsway						
Prestwick						
Tiree						

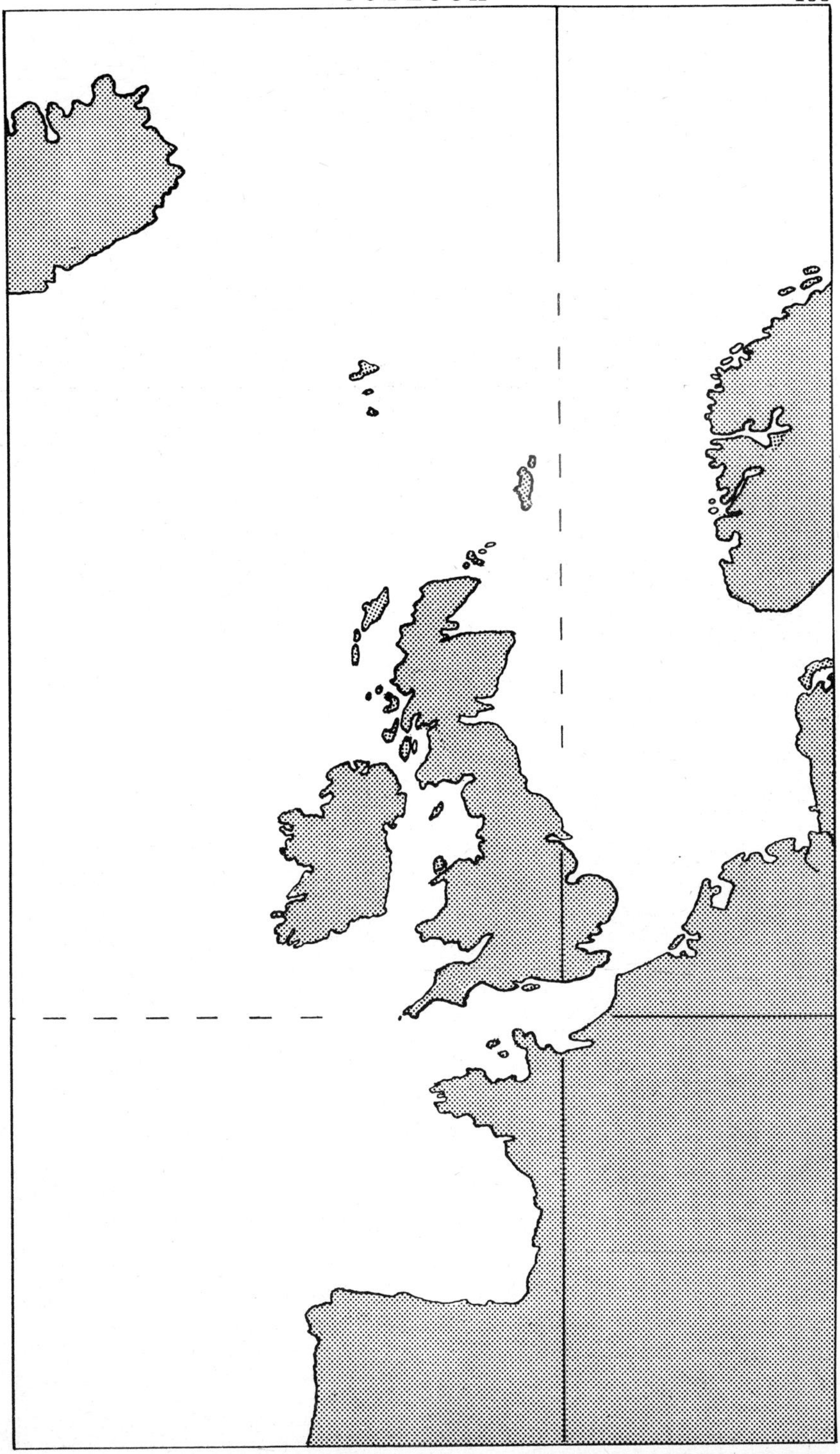

OUTLOOK

Weather Forecast Date: Time:

General Synopsis at G. M. T.

System	Present Position	Movement	Forecast Position	At

Forecast for Sea Areas

Area	Gales	Wind		Weather	Visibility
		Now	Later		
Viking					
Forties					
Cromarty					
Forth					
Tyne					
Dogger					
Fisher					
German Bight					
Humber					
Thames					
Smith's Knoll					
Dover					
Wight					
Portland					
Plymouth					
Biscay					
Finisterre					
Sole					
Lundy					
Fastnet					
Irish Sea					
Shannon					
Rockall					
Malin					
Hebrides					
Minches					
Fair Isle					
Bailey					
Faeroes					
S.E.Iceland					

Reports from Coastal Stations at G. M. T.

Station	Wind		Weather	Vis.	Baro.	Tendency
	Dir'n.	Force				
Wick						
Bell Rock						
Dowsing						
Galloper						
Royal Sovereign						
Portland Bill						
Scilly						
Valentia						
Ronaldsway						
Prestwick						
Tiree						

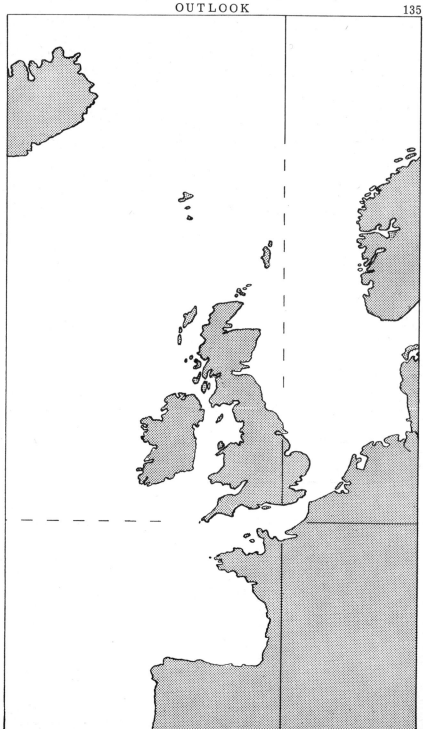

INDEX